8/5/84

o be awarded. Tur choi: of a 10-
n and Pans a week y. W uise to
 or a weekiong ho d.
  to 4 pe   s

SONGS OF PRAISE

Combined Edition

EDITOR'S NOTE

The *Songs of Praise* series was designed to meet the need in churches and prayer groups for legal songbooks containing effective and popular worship music from many copyright sources. These songs were selected for their ability to draw groups together in the worship of God and the sharing of his word.

Now, for the convenience of those who are encountering *Songs of Praise* for the first time and of those groups who need to replace copies or add to their present collections, Servant Music presents the *Combined Edition*.

In order to make the *Combined Edition* easy to use alongside the original songbooks, we have retained the original numbering system and song order. The songs within each volume section are arranged alphabetically and numbered 1-79 for *Volume 1*, 201-241 for *Volume 2*, 301-339 for *Volume 3*, and 401-428 for *Volume 4*. A complete title and first line index is located at the back of the book to aid in locating any particular song.

ACKNOWLEDGEMENTS

We wish to thank World Library Publications, Inc., F.E.L. Publications, Ltd., Mills Music, Inc., and all others who have given permission for their songs to be included in *Songs of Praise: Combined Edition*. Any errors or omissions will be cheerfully corrected in future printings.

Songs of Praise: Combined Edition and the four separate original volumes may be ordered from

Servant Publications
P.O. Box 8617
Ann Arbor, Michigan 48107
U.S.A.

Hardcover Edition: ISBN 0-89283-173-1
Paperback Edition: ISBN 0-89283-172-3

Illustrations by Peg Hosford

Compiled by **THE WORD OF GOD MUSIC**
Published by **SERVANT MUSIC**

TABLE OF CONTENTS

All of Your People

Words and Music by
James Berlucchi

REFRAIN
Capo 2, Play D

All of Your peo-ple say,__ "We love You." All of Your peo-ple cry,__ "Ho-

san-na!"___ With lift- ed hearts and voi-ces prais-ing, rais-ing songs of love to

You,___ just to You.___ *to verse* | just to You,___ just to You.___

Verses may be sung either in E major or in E minor. While the verses printed here may be sung,
is it customary to improvise verses following the chord progression given. The verses printed
here are given as examples of what may be done.
The verses in E major are especially appropriate for large gatherings, while the verses in E
minor may work best for very small groups or for private singing.

VERSES IN E MAJOR

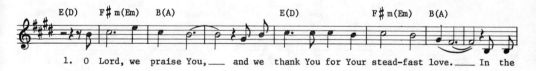

1. O Lord, we praise You,__ and we thank You for Your stead-fast love.__ In the

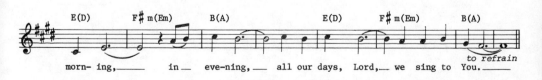

morn- ing,___ in__ eve-ning,__ all our days, Lord,__ we sing to You.___
to refrain

Continued ▶

2. To the Fa-ther we give all our praise.— To the Son we give our lives.— To the

Spir-it of God,——— thanks and hon-or—— and praise.— We de-light in You.———

to refrain

VERSES IN E MINOR

1. Who is like a son of man en- throned, His eyes— like burn-ing
2. Like a dia- mond, on the throne He's praised, the el- ders and the
3. Eve- ry na- tion, race, and tribe are there, Dressed in white they

flame, and His face———— a shin- ing sun?————
saints, sing- ing—— night and day.
stand, hold- ing palms—— in their——— hands.———

Who—— with a word did make— the world, up- hold- ing all cre-
"Ho-ly, Ho- ly, Ho- ly is— the Lord, the Al- might- y, He Who
Vic-t'ry to our God, Who sits— en- throned, and vic-t'ry to the

a- tion, with a voice— like the roar of the sea?———
was,—— He Who is— and— is to— come."———
Lamb,—— and all sing-ing ———— cry, "A- men!"———

to refrain

Allelu!

MILDRED (Mimi) ARMSTRONG

Liltingly

Solo 1. Come and bless, come and praise, come and praise the liv-ing God.
CHORUS Al - le - lu, Al - le - lu, Al - le - lu - ia, Je - sus Christ.

All Al - le - lu, Al - le - lu, Al - le - lu - ia, Je - sus Christ.
Al - le - lu, Al - le - lu, Al - le - lu - ia, Je - sus Christ.

2. Come and seek, come and find, come and find the living God.
   Allelu, Allelu, Alleluia, Jesus Christ.

3. Come and hear, come and know, come and know the living God.
   Allelu, Allelu, Alleluia, Jesus Christ.

4. Come and bless, come and praise, come and praise the Word of God.
   Word of God, Word made flesh, Alleluia, Jesus, Christ.

5. Come behold, come and see, come and see the newborn babe.
   Allelu, Allelu, Alleluia, Jesus Christ.

6. Angel choirs sing above, "Glory to the Son of God!"
   Shepherd folk sing below, "Allelu, Emmanuel!"

7. Allelu, Allelu, Allelu, Emmanuel!
   Allelu, Allelu, Allelu, Emmanuel!

3

Alleluia

Words and Music by
Jerry Sinclair

1. Al - le - lu - ia.____ Al - le - lu - ia.____ Al - le - lu - ia.____

____ Al - le - lu - ia.____ Al - le - lu - ia.____

Additional Verses: 2. Jesus is Lord.
3. My Redeemer.
4. Come, Lord Jesus.

4

Alleluia No. 1

Words and Music by
Donald Fishel

REFRAIN

Al - le - lu - ia, Al - le - lu - ia, give thanks to the ris - en Lord, Al - le

lu - ia, Al - le - lu - ia, give praise to His name.

VERSES

1. Je - sus is Lord of all the earth,
2. Spread the good news o'er all the earth,
3. We have been cru - ci - fied with Christ.
4. God has pro - claimed the just re - ward,
5. Come let us praise the liv - ing God.

He is the King of cre - a - tion.
Je - sus has died and has ris - en.
Now we shall live____ for ev - er.
life for all men, al - le - lu - ia.
joy - ful - ly sing to our Sav - ior.

Alleluia, Sons of God Arise

With flowing movement

Mimi Armstrong

Chorus: Al - le - lu - ia, Al - le - lu - ia, Al - le - lu - ia, Sons of God a - rise! Al - le - lu - ia, Al - le - lu - ia, Sons of God a - rise and fol - low the Lord.

1. Come and be clothed in His right - eous - ness, Come join the band who are called by His name.

2. Look at the world which is bound by sin, Walk in - to the midst of it pro - claim - ing My life.

6 The Angel of the Lord

Psalm 34:7-8

Unknown

The an-gel of the Lord__ en- camp-eth round a- bout them that fear him__

1. 2.

__ and de- liv-ers them.__ The __ Oh, taste and see that the Lord is__ good.

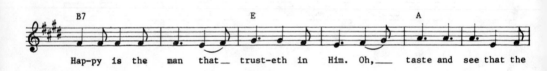

Hap-py is the man that__ trust-eth in Him. Oh,__ taste and see that the

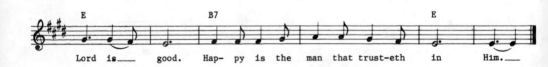

Lord is__ good. Hap-py is the man that trust-eth in Him.__

Away They Went With Weeping

Adapted from
Psalm 126 by J.J.C.

James J. Cavnar

A- way they went with weep-ing, car- ry- ing the seed;

back, they came back sing- ing with their sheaves.

They who sow in tears shall reap with laugh- ter;

they who sow in tears shall sing.

1. When Yah- weh brought Zi- on's____ cap- tives home, at
2. E- ven the pa- gans____ start- ed talk-ing a-
3. From bond- age____ Yah- weh, de-liv- er us____ as

first it__ seemed____ like a dream.____ Then our mouths__
bout the mar- vels the__ Lord had done. What____ mar- vels
streams in a des-ert____ land.____ Those who went out

filled__ with laugh-ter and our lips__ with song.__
He ____ did for us, and____ how we were glad!__
sow-ing in tears,____ they shall sing as they reap.__

G9

8 Balm in Gilead

Unknown

REFRAIN
Capo 3, Play D

There is a Balm in Gil-e-ad, to make the wound-ed whole.— There is a

Balm in Gil- e- ad, to heal the sin- sick soul.
to verse

VERSES

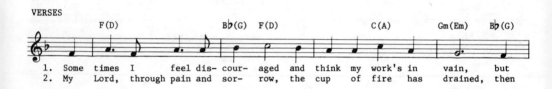

1. Some times I feel dis-cour- aged and think my work's in vain, but
2. My Lord, through pain and sor- row, the cup of fire has drained, then

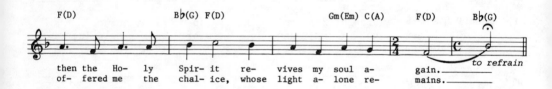

then the Ho- ly Spir- it re- vives my soul a- gain.
of- fered me the chal- ice, whose light a- lone re- mains.
to refrain

3. If you can-not pray like Pe- ter, if you can-not preach like Paul, go

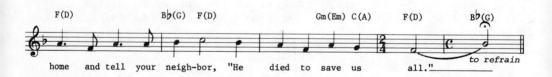

home and tell your neigh-bor, "He died to save us all."
to refrain

Bless the Lord, O My Soul

Psalm 103:1

Unknown

Bless the Lord, O my soul.___ Bless the Lord, O my soul.___ Let

all___ that is with- in me bless His ho- ly name.____

Public domain

The Breath of God

Words and Music by
William E. Booth-Clibborn

Let it breathe on me, let it breathe on me. Let this

breath of God now breathe on me. Let it breathe on me, let it

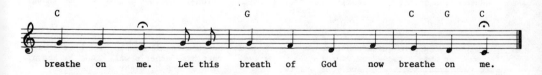

breathe on me. Let this breath of God now breathe on me.

11 Canticle of the Gift

Text: Refrain by Pat Uhl
Verses by Michael Gilligan

Music by
Pat Uhl

REFRAIN

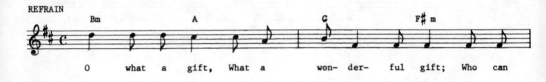

O what a gift, What a won-der-ful gift; Who can

tell the won-ders of the Lord? Let us o-pen our eyes, our

ears, and our hearts; it is Christ the Lord, it is He!

to verse

VERSES

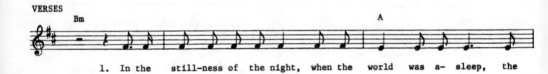

1. In the still-ness of the night, when the world was a-sleep, the

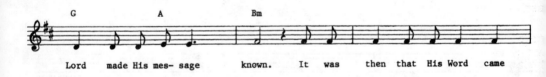

Lord made His mes-sage known. It was then that His Word came

down from on high, from the Fa-ther's roy-al throne: Christ our Lord and our King!

to refrain

2. His mighty Word cuts quick and clean,
far sharper than a two-edged sword:
Open your eyes, your ears, and your hearts,
and hear the Word of the Lord:
Christ our Lord and our King!

3. He came to his people, the chosen race,
that his Father's will would be known;
Lion of Judah, Light of the World,
our Redeemer came to his own:
Christ our Lord and our King!

6. He lived here among us, he worked here among us,
morning, night, and day;
Showed us his glory, gave us a promise,
and then we turned away:
Christ our Lord and our King!

At the Passover meal on the night before he died,
he lifted up his eyes and prayed
Then he broke the bread, then he shared the wine--
the gift that God had made:
Christ our Lord and our King!

On the hill of Calvary, the world held its breath;
and there for the world to see,
the Father gave his Son, his very own Son
for the love of you and me:
Christ our Lord and our King!

7. Early on that morning when the guards were sleeping,
the Father revealed his might;
Christ in his glory arose from the dead,
the Lord of Life and Light:
Christ our Lord and our King!

8. On the road to Emmayus, the glory that is his,
the disciples could never see.
Then he broke the bread, then he shared the wine;
it is the Lord, it is he:
Christ our Lord and our King!

9. Now look around you and open your eyes;
remember the Spirit is here.
Here within his Church, his people are one.
Look, the Lord is near:
Christ our Lord and our King!

Canticle of the Three Young Men   12

Verses adapted from Daniel 3
REFRAIN
Capo 2, Play G

Music and Refrain by
an anonymous Canadian

Bless the Lord, all you works of the Lord. Praise Him! Ex-alt Him for- ev- er!

VERSES

1. Sun and moon, bless the Lord. Stars of the heav-ens, bless the Lord.

Speed-ing light, bless the Lord. Praise Him! Ex- alt Him for- ev- er!

2. Moun- tains and hills, bless the Lord. Light-ning and clouds, bless the Lord.
3. Seas and riv- ers, bless the Lord. Birds of the air, bless the Lord.
4. Young men and maid-ens, bless the Lord. Sons of men, bless the Lord.

Let the earth bless the Lord. Praise Him! Ex-alt Him for- ev- er!
Beasts and cat-tle, bless the Lord. Praise Him! Ex-alt Him for- ev- er!
Ser-vants of the Lord, bless the Lord. Praise Him! Ex-alt Him for- ev- er!

13 Come All Ye Nations

Come, Follow Me

14

Words and Music by
Ann Cadwallader

15   Come, Go With Me to That Land

Unknown

Come, go with me to that land. Come, go with me to that land. Come, go
with me to that land where I'm bound.___ Come, go with me to that land. Come, go
with me to that land, to that land, to that land where I'm bound.___

Any of the following verses, or spontaneous verses, may also be used.

Be singing and dancing in that land . . .
There's milk and honey in that land . . .
You're gonna meet Jesus in that land . . .
Well, don't you know heaven is that land . . .

16   Come Holy Ghost

Veni Creator Spiritus
Rabanus Maurus, 776-856 (?)
Tr. Edward Caswall, 1849, alt.

Louis Lambillotte, S. J.

1. Come, Ho - ly Ghost, Cre - a - tor blest,
2. O Com-fort blest, to thee we cry,
3. Praise be to thee, Fa - ther and Son,

1. And in our hearts take up thy rest;
2. Thou heav'n - ly Gift of God most High;
3. And Ho - ly Spir - it, Three in One;

1. Come with thy grace and heav'n - ly aid
2. Thou Font of life, and Fire of love,
3. And may the Son on us be - stow

1. To fill the hearts which thou hast made. made.
2. And sweet A - noint - ing from a - bove. bove.
3. The gifts that from the Spir - it flow. flow.

Consider the Lilies

17

Matthew 6:25-34
Adapted by Jean Goeboro

Music by Jean Goeboro

REFRAIN

Con - si - der the lil - ies of __ the field; they nei-ther toil nor spin.__ Yet

I tell you that ev-en Sol - o - mon was not __ ar - rayed like these. these.__

to verse

1. What shall we   eat, Lord? What shall we   drink? What shall we   put on   to - day?
2. The birds of   the   air   don't toil or   reap,   yet   our good   Fa - ther feeds them.
3. If God so clothes the   grass of the   field,   which is   a - live and   then burned,
4. Do not be   anx - ious   for to - mor - row.   Let each day's trou - ble   suf - fice.

Is not life more than food,__ the bod - y   more than clothes?__
Are you not of   more worth __   in   the   eyes   of   God? __
will the Lord not much more __   give clothes   to   His   chil - dren? __
Seek first His king - dom,__   and   all   things will   be   yours. __

18 The Dancing Heart

Words and Music by
Roy Turner

REFRAIN

Oh, the Ho-ly Ghost will set your feet a danc-ing,____ the Ho-ly Ghost will

thrill you thru and thru;____ the Ho-ly Ghost will set your feet a

danc-ing,____ and set your heart a danc-ing too.____

VERSES

1. Da- vid danced be- fore the Lord, he danced with all his might, His
2. Da- vid danced be- fore the Lord to mag- ni- fy His name; In
3. Out of E- gypt long a- go, the Is- rael- ites were led;
4. There was a cel- e- bra- tion ____ up- on the Red Sea shore;
5. The prod-i- gal was far a- way, ____ wan- d'ring out in sin, But
6. The fa- ther's house with mu- sic rang to wel- come home the son;
7. Now man- y saints are cold and bound by un- be- lief to- day, They
8. Now in the Bi- ble we can read that in the lat- ter days,

1. heart was filled with Ho- ly joy, his spir-it was so light;
2. God's al- might- y pres- ence, ____ he felt no sense of shame; The
3. By a might- y mir- a- cle they all were kept and fed;
4. Tim- brels rang, ____ des- ert sands be- came a danc- ing floor; The
5. he came back to Fa- ther's house and Fa- ther took him in; He
6. Wine was flow- ing full and free, all mis- er- y was gone; The
7. want the bless- ings of the Lord but wor- ry what men say; Oh,
8. Men would leave their first love ____ and turn to car- nal ways; But

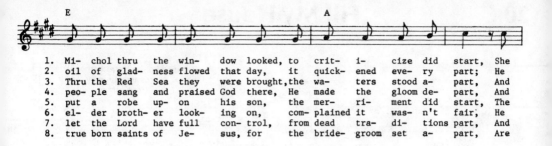

	E								A							

1. Mi- chol thru the win- dow looked, to crit- i- cize did start, She
2. oil of glad- ness flowed that day, it quick- ened eve- ry part; He
3. Thru the Red Sea they were brought, the wa- ters stood a- part, And
4. peo- ple sang and praised God there, He made the gloom de- part, And
5. put a robe up- on his son, the mer- ri- ment did start, The
6. el- der broth- er look- ing on, com- plained it was- n't fair; He
7. let the Lord have full con- trol, from dead tra- di- tions part, And
8. true born saints of Je- sus, for the bride- groom set a- part, Are

	B7								E		B7		E			

to refrain

1. did- n't know that Da- vid_____ had got a danc-ing heart.
2. had- n't on- ly danc- ing feet, he had a danc-ing heart.
3. God gave sis- ter Mir- i- am, a dance down in her heart.
4. put a dance of love and joy, a- deep down in their hearts.
5. prod- i- gal got danc- ing shoes, to match his danc-ing heart.
6. had- n't got a danc- ing heart, like all the oth- ers there.
7. He will set you free with- in, you'll have a danc-ing heart.
8. wait-ing for His com- ing, with a joy- ful danc-ing heart.

Father, I Adore You   19

Words and Music by
Terrye Coelho

1. Fa- ther, I a- dore you, lay my life be- fore you. How I love you.
2. Je- sus, I a- dore you, lay my life be- fore you. How I love you.
3. Spir- it, I a- dore you, lay my life be- fore you. How I love you.

20 Fill My House

from "Songs Of Brotherhood"
Words and Music by
Peter Kearney

Capo 3, Play A

1. Fill my house ____ un - to the full - est. Eat my
(2) time ____ un - to the full - est. Find in
(3) Lord, ____ with love e - nor - mous, from the
(4) me, ____ as one in Christ - love. May our

bread ____ and drink my wine ____ The love I
me the trust you seek. ____ Take my
cross ____ this les - son taught: ____ love all
hearts ____ all beat as one. ____ May we

bear ____ is held from no one. All I have ____ and all I
hands ____ to you out - reach ing. All I have ____ and all I
men ____ as I have loved you. All I have ____ and all I
give ____ our - selves com - plete ly. All I have ____ and all I

last time only

do ____ I give to you. ____ 2. Take my
do ____ I give to you. ____ 3. Christ our
do ____ I give to you. ____ 4. Join with
do ____ I give to you. ____ *repeat verse 1* 1. Fill my

The Foot Washing Song

21

Adapted from
John 13

Words and Music by
Shirley Lewis Brown

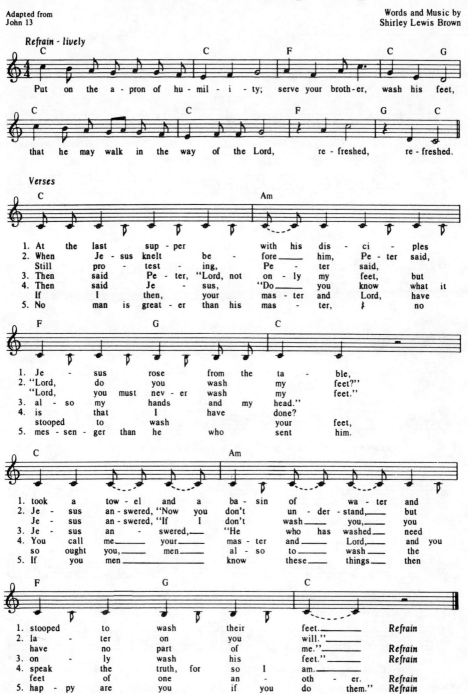

22 For You Are My God

Words and Music by
John B. Foley, S.J.

REFRAIN

For you are my God. You a - lone are my joy; de - fend me, O Lord.

VERSES

1. You give mar-vel-ous com-rades to me: the faith-ful who dwell in your land; those who choose a - li - en gods have cho-sen an a - li - en band.

2. You are my por-tion and cup; it is you that I claim for my prize. Your her - i - tage is my de - light: the lot you have giv-en to me.

3. Glad are my heart and my soul; se - cure-ly my bod - y shall rest. For you will not leave me for dead; nor lead your be - lov-ed a - stray.

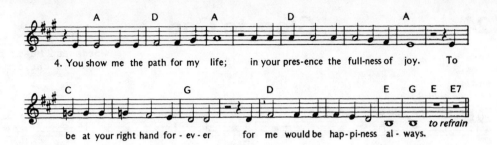

4. You show me the path for my life; in your pres-ence the full-ness of joy. To
be at your right hand for - ev - er for me would be hap-pi-ness al - ways.

Glorious God

23

Words and Music by
Sebastian Temple

VERSES Praise, hon-or, and glo-ry are yours. Praise, hon-or, and glo-ry are yours.

1. Glo - ri - ous God, _____ King of cre - a - tion, _____ we praise you, we
2. Glo - ri - ous God, _____ mag - ni - fi - cent, ho - ly, _____ we love you, a -
3. Glo - ri - ous God, _____ King of cre - a - tion, _____ we praise you, we

bless you, we wor-ship you in song; Glo - ri - ous God, _____ in ad - o
dore you, we come to you in prayer. Glo - ri - ous God, _____ might-y e -
bless you, we wor-ship you in song; Glo - ri - ous God, _____ in ad - o

ra - tion, _____ at your feet we be - long. _____ to refrain
ter - nal, _____ we sing your praise ev - 'ry - where. _____ to refrain
ra - tion, _____ at your feet we be - long. _____ to coda

REFRAIN

Lord of life, _____ Fa-ther al - might - y. Lord of hearts, _____

_____ Christ the King. _____ Lord of love, _____ Ho - ly

Spir - it, _____ to whom we hom - age bring. _____ to verse

Praise, hon-or, and glo-ry are yours. Praise hon-or and glo-ry are yours. _____

24 Glory to God

Words and Music by
Charles Christmas

REFRAIN
Capo 2, Play D

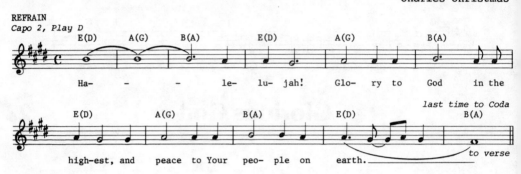

Ha - - le- lu- jah! Glo- ry to God in the

last time to Coda

high-est, and peace to Your peo- ple on earth._____ *to verse*

VERSES

1. Fa - - - - ther, O Fa- ther, all
2. Je - - sus,_____ Je- sus, Je- sus,_____
3. Spir - it,_____ Spir- it of God,_____
4. With all the saints who have gone on be- fore us,_____

glo - ry__ be- longs_____ to You._____
we give_____ our hearts_____ to You._____
Ho - ly coun- sel- lor,_____
with all__ of Your an- gels in cho- rus.__

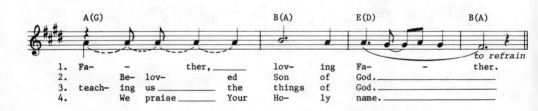

1. Fa - ther,_____ lov- ing Fa - ther.
2. Be- lov- ed Son of God._____
3. teach- ing us_____ the things of God._____
4. We praise_____ Your Ho- ly name._____ *to refrain*

Glo- ry to God!_____

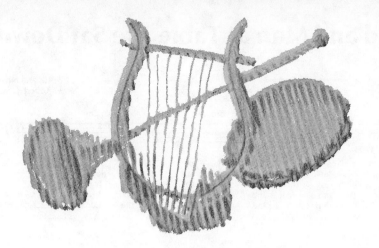

Glory to God, Glory

25

Words and Music by
Clarence Jos. Rivers

Capo 3, Play E

1 Praise Christ, the Son of the liv - ing God! *to refrain*

REFRAIN Glo - ry to God, glo - ry, O praise Him, al - le - lu - ia!

Glo - ry to God, glo - ry, O praise the name of the Lord!

2 Praise Christ, the Word of the liv - ing God! *to refrain*

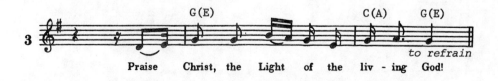

3 Praise Christ, the Light of the liv - ing God! *to refrain*

26 God and Man at Table Are Sat Down

Words and Music by
Rev. Robert J. Stamps

	Em	Bm	Em

1. O,   wel-come   all   ye   no - ble   saints of   old,_____   as
2.   El - ders,   mar - tyrs,   all   are   fall - ing   down;_____
3.   Who   is   this who   spreads the   vic - t'ry   feast?_____
4.   Beg - gars,   lame, and   har - lots   al - so   here;_____   re -
5.   Wor - ship   in   the   pres - ence   of the   Lord,_____   with
6.   When at   last   this   earth shall   pass a - way, _____   when

	D	A7	D	D7	Em

now be - fore your ver - y   eyes un - fold _____ the   won - ders all   so
proph-ets,   pa - tri - archs are   gath - 'ring 'round,_____ what   an - gels longed   to
Who   is   this who makes our   war - ring   cease?_____   Je - sus,   Ris - en
pen - tant   pub - li - cans are   draw - ing   near; _____   way - ward sons   come
joy - ful   songs and   hearts in   one   ac - cord,_____ and   let our   Host   at
Je - sus   and   His   bride are   one   to   stay,_____   the feast of   love   is

Continued ▶

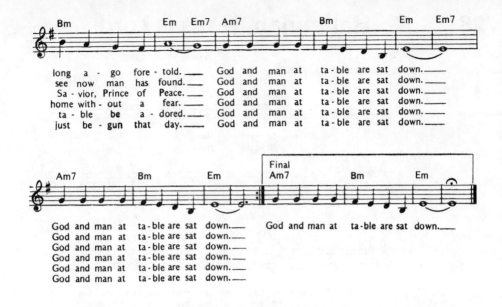

long a - go fore - told. ___ God and man at ta - ble are sat down. ___
see now man has found. ___ God and man at ta - ble are sat down. ___
Sa - vior, Prince of Peace. ___ God and man at ta - ble are sat down. ___
home with - out a fear. ___ God and man at ta - ble are sat down. ___
ta - ble be a - dored. ___ God and man at ta - ble are sat down. ___
just be - gun that day. ___ God and man at ta - ble are sat down. ___

Final

God and man at ta - ble are sat down. ___ God and man at ta - ble are sat down. ___
God and man at ta - ble are sat down. ___
God and man at ta - ble are sat down. ___
God and man at ta - ble are sat down. ___
God and man at ta - ble are sat down. ___
God and man at ta - ble are sat down. ___

Hallelujah, I Want to Sing All About It 27

Words and Music by
Roy Turner

Hal- le- lu- jah, ___ I want to sing all a- bout it, Hal- le- lu- jah, ___ I want to

shout all a-bout it. Hal-le- lu- jah, ___ I can't live with-out ___ it, Praise God, ___ Praise

God; ___ Now I'm liv-ing in a new cre-a- tion, Now I'm drink-ing at the

well of sal-va- tion. Now there is no con- dem-na- tion, Praise God! ___

28   Hallelujah, Jesus Is Lord

M.A.F.   Mimi Armstrong Farra

With rhythmic boldness
Refrain

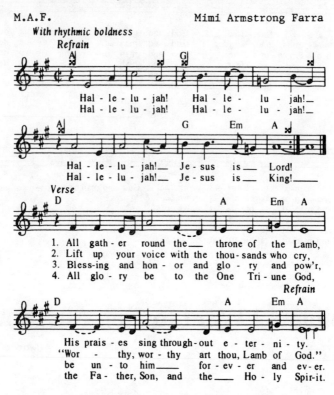

Hal - le - lu - jah! Hal - le - lu - jah!_
Hal - le - lu - jah! Hal - le - lu - jah!_

Hal - le - lu - jah!_ Je - sus is _ Lord!
Hal - le - lu - jah!_ Je - sus is _ King!_

Verse

1. All gath - er round the _ throne of the Lamb,
2. Lift up your voice with the thou - sands who cry,
3. Bless - ing and hon - or and glo - ry and pow'r,
4. All glo - ry be to the One Tri - une God,

Refrain

His prais - es sing through - out e - ter - ni - ty.
"Wor - thy, wor - thy art thou, Lamb of God."
be un - to him_ for - ev - er and ev - er.
the Fa - ther, Son, and the_ Ho - ly Spir - it.

29   He Is Lord

Words and Music by
Marvin V. Frey

He is Lord._ He is Lord._ He is ris - en from the dead, and He is

Lord!_ Eve - ry knee shall bow, and eve - ry

tongue con - fess _ that Je - sus Christ is Lord!_

Here Comes Jesus

Unknown

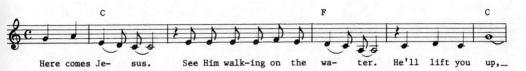

Here comes Je- sus. See Him walk-ing on the wa- ter. He'll lift you up,__

__ and He'll help you to stand._____ Here comes Je- sus. He's the mas-ter of the

waves that roll.____ Here comes Je- sus.__ He'll make you whole._____ Here comes

2nd time: D G D A   D D7 G D A D   4th time: F B♭ F C   F F7 B♭ F C F

3rd time: E A E B7   E E7 A E B7 E   5th time: G C G D   G G7 C G D G

FINAL ENDING

Here comes Je- sus.__   He'll make you__   whole.

__ Here comes Je- sus.   He'll save your   soul!__

31 His Banner Over Me Is Love

Words and Music by
Alfred B. Smith

I'm my be-lov-ed's and He is mine. His ban-ner o-ver me is love.

I'm my be-lov-ed's and He is mine. His ban-ner o-ver me is love.

I'm my be-lov-ed's and He is mine. His ban-ner o-ver me is

love. His ban-ner o-ver me___ is love.___

Any of the following verses, or spontaneous verses, may also be used.

He fills me full of holy joy . . .
In Him I am a new creation . . .
He welcomes me to His banqueting table . . .
He lifts us up to heavenly places . . .
He makes straight paths before my feet . . .
/ Jesus is the rock of my salvation . . .
He calls us to the Body of Christ . . .
He builds His church on a firm foundation . . .
We hear Him say, "Lay down your life." . . .

How Great Is Our God

Unknown

How great is our God!____ How great is His name!____

____ How great is our God!____ For - ev - er the same. ____

____ He rolled back __ the wa - ters _____ of the might - y Red

Sea, _____ and He said, "I'll nev - er leave_____ you.

Put your trust in Me."_____

Public domain

33 Hymn For a Prayer Meeting

Words and Music by
Ed Keefe
Mike Fitzgerald

REFRAIN
Capo 3, Play Am

Al - le - lu - ia, praise the Lord! Shout to God_ on_ high!

From the ver - y depths of_ earth His_ ho - ly_ name_ we_ cry.

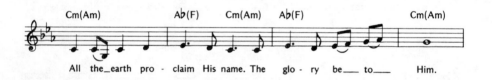

All the_earth pro - claim His name. The glo - ry be_ to_ Him.

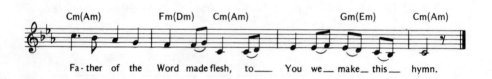

Fa - ther of the Word made flesh, to_ You we_ make_ this_ hymn.

VERSES

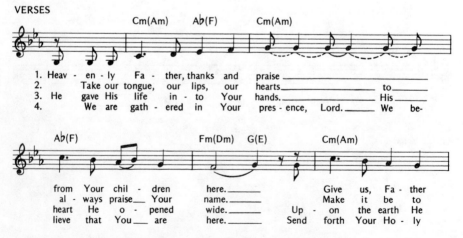

1. Heav - en - ly Fa - ther, thanks and praise _____
2. Take our tongue, our lips, our hearts _____ to _____
3. He gave His life in - to Your hands. _____ His _____
4. We are gath - ered in Your pres - ence, Lord. _____ We be -

from Your chil - dren here. _____ Give us, Fa - ther
al - ways praise_ Your name. _____ Make it be to
heart He o - pened wide. _____ Up - on the earth He
lieve that You_ are here. _____ Send forth Your Ho - ly

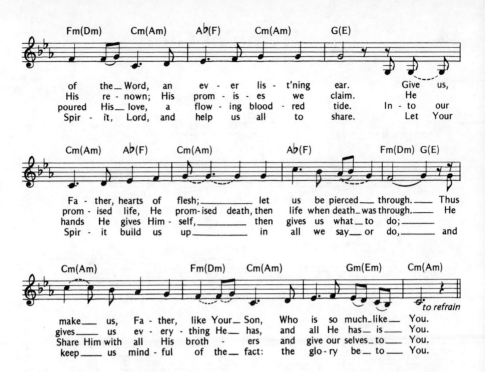

Fm(Dm)   Cm(Am)   A♭(F)   Cm(Am)   G(E)

of the_ Word, an ev - er lis - t'ning ear. Give us,
His re - nown; His prom - is - es we claim. He
poured His_ love, a flow - ing blood - red tide. In - to our
Spir - it, Lord, and help us all to share. Let Your

Cm(Am)   A♭(F)   Cm(Am)   A♭(F)   Fm(Dm) G(E)

Fa - ther, hearts of flesh;___ let us be pierced_ through. Thus
prom - ised life, He prom-ised death, then life when death_ was through.___ He
hands He gives Him - self,___ then gives us what_ to do;___
Spir - it build us up___ in all we say_ or do,___ and

Cm(Am)   Fm(Dm)   Cm(Am)   Gm(Em)   Cm(Am)

to refrain

make_ us, Fa - ther, like Your_ Son, Who is so much_ like_ You.
gives_ us ev - ery - thing He_ has, and all He has_ is _ You.
Share Him with all His broth - ers and give our selves_ to_ You.
keep_ us mind - ful of the_ fact: the glo - ry be - to_ You.

34   Hymn of Glory

Words and Music by
Charles Christmas

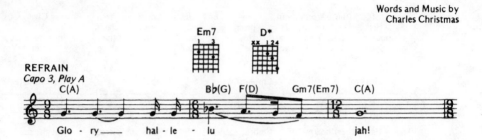

REFRAIN
Capo 3, Play A

Glo - ry ___ hal - le - lu - jah!

Glo - ry ___ hal - le - lu - jah! ___

1. Give thanks to our God___ and let him be praised, ___ with
2. His word ev - er true, the Son of his love.
3. Wor - thy the Lamb who was slain for our sins. ___ He
4. Ho - ly ho - ly the Lord God Al - might - y who

sanc - ti - fied hearts___ and hands that are raised. ___
Sing men of earth to the heav - ens a - bove. ___
laid down His life,___ He rose up a - gain. ___
was, who is, ___ and who is to come. In

Come join a song ___ of praise to our God.
Hon - or and glo - ry be - long to our God.
To us He gives ___ un - end - ing life.
glo - ry come, ___ Lord Je - sus, come.

Hymn of the Universe

Words by
Ed Keefe

Music by
Mike Fitzgerald

VERSES

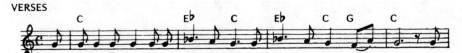

1. Who watch-es the wind as the birds fly out to greet the ris - ing___ sun? Who
2. Who watch-es the world as the sun rolls on to charge the roar - ing___ stars? Who
3. Who pac-es the wave of a burst of light to make us all stand___ still? Who

watch-es the rain as the clouds pour in to meet the ris - en___ earth?
plays out the hymn of a spin - ning cloud to keep us on the___ run?
puls - es the note of a hun - dred hearts to move us on the___ march?

REFRAIN

Gal-ax - y build-er, Lord Je-sus the King, give us this day the bread that we need.

Feed us in heav-en the wheat of the fields. Give us to oth - ers in

FINAL ENDING

hun-dred-fold___ yields. ___ *to verse* Gal-ax - y build-er, Lord Je-sus the King! ___

36   I Am the Bread of Life

Based on John 6 and 11

Words and Music by
Sr. M. Suzanne Toolan, S.M.

Capo 1, Play G

1. I am the bread of life; He who comes to me shall not hun-ger. He who be-lieves in me shall not thirst. No one can come to me un - less the Fa-ther draw him.

REFRAIN

And I will raise____ him up,____and I will raise____ him up,____ and I will raise____ him up____ on the last____ day. day, and I will day.____

2. The bread that I will give is my flesh for the life of the world,____ and he who eats of this bread, he shall live for - ev - er, he shall live for - ev - er.

3. Un - less____ you eat of the flesh of the Son of Man, and drink of His blood, and drink of His blood, you shall not have life with - in you.

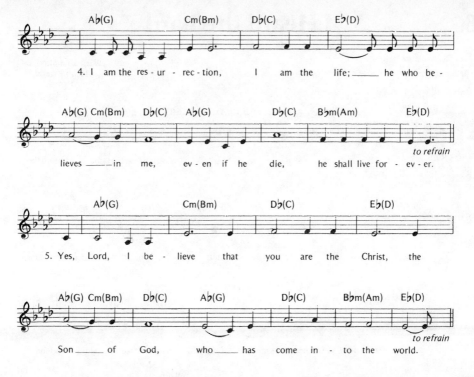

4. I am the res-ur-rec-tion, I am the life; ___ he who be-

lieves ___ in me, ev-en if he die, he shall live for-ev-er.

to refrain

5. Yes, Lord, I be-lieve that you are the Christ, the

Son ___ of God, who ___ has come in-to the world.

to refrain

I Have Decided to Follow Jesus   37

Unknown

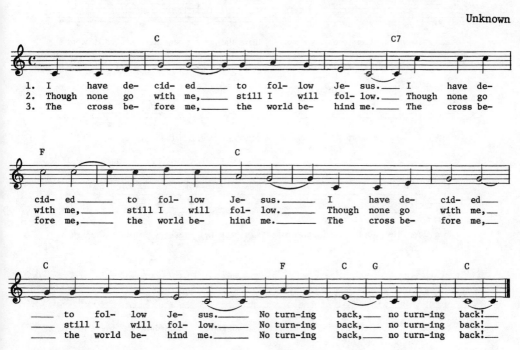

1. I have de-cid-ed ___ to fol-low Je-sus. ___ I have de-
2. Though none go with me, ___ still I will fol-low. ___ Though none go
3. The cross be-fore me, ___ the world be-hind me. ___ The cross be-

cid-ed ___ to fol-low Je-sus. ___ I have de-cid-ed ___
with me, ___ still I will fol-low. ___ Though none go with me, ___
fore me, ___ the world be-hind me. ___ The cross be-fore me, ___

___ to fol-low Je-sus. ___ No turn-ing back, ___ no turn-ing back!
___ still I will fol-low. ___ No turn-ing back, ___ no turn-ing back!
___ the world be-hind me. ___ No turn-ing back, ___ no turn-ing back!

I Heard the Lord

Words and Music by
Jacob Krieger

Capo 4, Play C

I heard the Lord   call my   name.   Lis-ten   close, you'll hear the same.   I heard the

Lord   call my name.   Lis-ten   close, you'll hear the same.   I heard the Lord   call my name.

—— Lis-ten close, you'll hear the same.   Take His   hand;   we are glo-ry   bound.

—— His word is   love; love's his word: that's the mes - sage that I   heard. His word is

love;   love's His   word: that's the mes - sage that I   heard. His word is

love; love's His   word: that's the mes - sage that I   heard. Take His   hand; we are glory

bound.   Place your hand in His and   you will know;   He will show you where to go. ——

39 I Want to Walk as a Child of the Light

Words and Music by
Kathleen Thomerson

VERSES

1. I want to walk as a child of the light. I want to fol- low
2. I want to see___ the bright-ness of God. I want to look at
3. I'm look-ing for___ the com- ing of Christ. I want to be with

Je- sus. God set the stars to give light to the world. The
Je- sus. Clear sun of right-eous- ness, shine on my path, and
Je- sus. When we have run___ with pa- tience the race, we

REFRAIN

star of my life___ is Je- sus. In Him there is no dark-ness at
show me the way to the Fa- ther.
shall know the joy___ of Je- sus.

all, the night and the day are both a- like. The Lamb is the light of the

cit- y of God. Shine in my heart, Lord Je- sus. A- men.

to verse

40 I Will Arise

Words and Music by
Mimi Armstrong Farra

Refrain

I will a- rise so ear- ly in the mor- ning,

rise to___ sing my Sa- vior's___ prais- es;

After the last refrain, the refrain and verse two may be sung
simultaneously observing the Coda

41 I Will Sing of the Mercies of the Lord

J. H. Fillmore

I will sing of the mer-cies of the Lord for-ev-er, I will

sing, I will sing. I will sing of the mer-cies of the Lord.

With my mouth__ will I make known Thy faith-ful-ness, Thy faith-ful-ness. With my

mouth__ will I make known Thy faith-ful-ness to all gen-er-a-tions. I will

42 In My Father's House

Unknown

1. Come and go with me to my Fa-ther's house, to my Fa-ther's house,

to my Fa-ther's house. Come and go with me

to my Fa-ther's house, where there's joy, joy, joy!

Any of the following verses, or spontaneous verses, may be used.

2. It's not very far to my Father's house . . .
3. Jesus is the Way to my Father's house . . .
4. Jesus is the Light in my Father's house . . .
5. All is peace and love in my Father's house . . .
6. We will dance and sing in my Father's house . . .
7. We will praise the Lord in my Father's house . . .

43 Israel, Rely on Yahweh

based on Psalm 130(131), M.F.

Mike Fitzgerald

REFRAIN
Capo 3, Play A

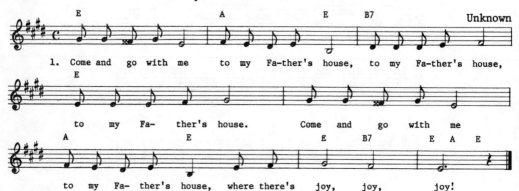

Is-ra-el, re-ly on Yah-weh now and for-ev-er-more.__ *to verse*

VERSES

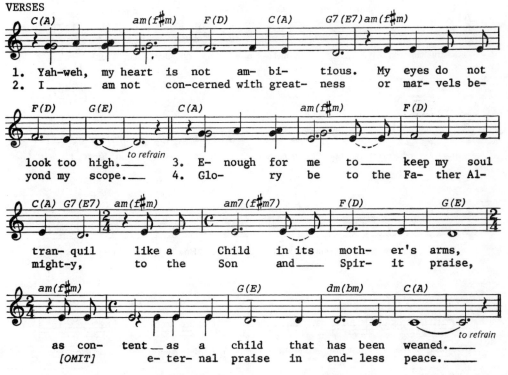

1. Yah-weh, my heart is not am-bi-tious. My eyes do not
2. I___ am not con-cerned with great-ness or mar-vels be-

look too high. *to refrain* 3. E-nough for me to___ keep my soul
yond my scope.___ 4. Glo-ry be to the Fa-ther Al-

tran-quil like a Child in its moth-er's arms,
might-y, to the Son and___ Spir-it praise,

as con-tent___as a child that has been weaned.___ *to refrain*
[OMIT] e-ter-nal praise in end-less peace.___

44 It Is Good to Give Thanks to the Lord

Psalm 91 (92)

Music by
Robert Twynham

It is good to give thanks to the Lord,——— to sing praise to your name,——— Most High,——— to pro - claim——— your kind - ness at dawn,——— and your faith - ful - ness through - out the night,——— with ten - stringed in - stru - ment and lyre,——— with mel - o - dy up - on the harp.——— For——— you make me glad, O Lord, by your deeds;——— at the works of your hands I re - joice.——— How great are your works, O Lord!——— How ver - y deep are your thoughts!——— The——— just man shall flour - ish like the palm tree,——— like a

ce - dar of Le - ba - non shall he grow. ____ They that are plant - ed

in the house of the Lord ____ shall flour - ish in the courts of our

God. ____ They shall bear fruit e - ven in old age; ____ vig - or -

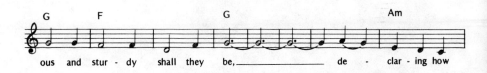

ous and stur - dy shall they be, ____ de - clar - ing how

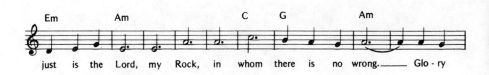

just is the Lord, my Rock, in whom there is no wrong. ____ Glo - ry

be to the Fa - ther, and to the Son, and to the Ho - ly Spir - ____

____ it. As it was in the be - gin - ning, is now, and ev - er shall

be, world with - out end. A men! ____

It's a Brand New Day

P.Q.

Paul Quinlan

45

1. It's a brand new day,_____ ev - 'ry - thing is fine._____
2. Well the heav'ns de - clare_____ in a way so grand;_____
3. His law of love,_____ it is whol - ly wise._____

_____ Though it may be gray, I want you to know that the sun's gon - na
_____ If the skies are fair or wind - y or gray, it's the work of His
_____ Word_____ from a - bove gives joy to my heart and it's light to my

shine._____ And out of that sky,_____ pierc - ing ev - er - y cloud___
hands._____ And down on that ground,_____ with_____ nev - er a word,
eyes._____ It's rich - es are fine_____ out_____ last - ing all days.

_____ is our God on high._____ There will be a new heart for ev - er - y
_____ such a might - y sound._____ And the morn - ing will see the roll - ing
_____ to the end of time._____ Though I walk in the path of e - vil

man like the flow - ers that come in ear - ly Spring. For ev - er - y
sun as he hap - pi - ly ris - es o'er the land; A mes - sen - ger
ways and my thoughts are a pres - ence caus - ing pain There's al - ways the

life there is___ a plan no mat - ter what au - tumn breez - es bring.
on his dai - ly run bring news of a Fa - ther's guid - ing hand.
sun of fu - ture days that fol - lows a time of wind and rain.

So put a - way cares, let free - dom be yours. Joy is ev - er - y - where,

joy is ev - er - y - where._____ Let free - dom ring, Al - le - lu - ia now

ev - 'ry - bod - y_____ sing, let our voi - ces shout to a might - y King.

46 Jacob's Song

Words and Music by
Jacob Krieger

Capo 4, Play C

Sing praise to the Lord for - ev - er and ev - er.

Sing praise to the Lord for- ev - er and ev - er.

Call un - to Him for hope in sal - va - tion.

Call un - to Him for hope in sal - va - tion. Sing praise al - le - lu - ia, sing praise al - le - lu. Sing

Sing praise al - le - lu - ia, sing praise al - le - lu. Sing

praise al - le - lu - ia, sing praise, al - le - lu. Call un - to Him. Call un -

praise al - le - lu - ia, sing praise al - le - lu. Call un - to Him. Call un -

Fine

to His name. Sing praise to the Lamb, for life ev - er - last -

to His name. Sing

ing. Call un - to Je - sus, call un - to the

praise to the Lamb, for life ev - er - last - ing.

Lord.   Sing praise al - le - lu - ia, sing
Call un-to Je-sus, call un - to the Lord. Sing praise al - le - lu - ia, sing
praise al - le - lu. Sing praise al - le - lu - ia, sing praise al - le - lu.   All sing   praise to our
praise al - le - lu. Sing praise al - le - lu - ia, sing praise al - le - lu.   All sing   praise to our

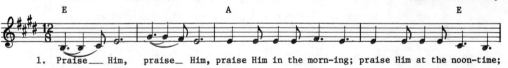

Fa - ther in   hea-ven.   To the Son and   Spir - it sing   praise! _____
Fa - ther in   hea-ven.   To the Son and   Spir - it sing   praise! _____

D.C. al Fine

Jesus in the Morning   47

Words and Music by
Marvin V. Frey

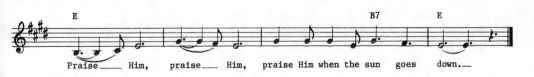

1. Praise___ Him,   praise__ Him, praise Him in the morn-ing; praise Him at the noon-time;

Praise___ Him,   praise___ Him,   praise Him when the sun   goes   down.___

Any of the following verses, or spontaneous verses, may also be used.

2. Jesus, Jesus, Jesus in the morning . . .
3. Serve Him, serve Him, serve Him in the morning . . .
4. Love Him, love Him, love Him in the morning . . .
5. Thank Him, thank Him, thank Him in the morning . . .

48   Jesus Is the One Who Saves

Words and Music by
James Berlucchi

1. All glo-ry to the Fa-ther of life.__ Praise be to the Ho-ly Spir-it,__
and to the shin-ing light of this world.__ Je-sus is the one who saves.__

2. You're the first-born of all of the sons,__ king__ of the new cre-a-tion.__
You're the bro-ther who makes us all one.__ Je-sus is the one who saves.__

3. Thank you Je-sus for ris-ing for us,__ the Fa-ther's love com-plete and glo-rious.__
Now we claim the vic-t'ry You give to us.__ Je-sus is the one who saves.__

4. Just call up-on the name of the Lord.__ Ask Him for His Ho-ly Spir-it.__
You'll find the one truth of this world.__ Je-sus is the one who saves.__

Je-sus is the one who saves.__ Je-sus is the one who saves.__

Words by
Fr. Willard Jabusch

Israeli Folk Melody

REFRAIN

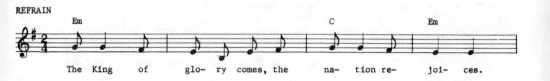

The King of glo- ry comes, the na- tion re- joi- ces.

O- pen the gates be- fore him, lift up your voi- ces.

VERSES

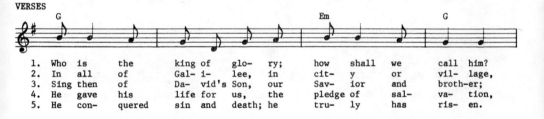

1. Who is the king of glo- ry; how shall we call him?
2. In all of Gal- i- lee, in cit- y or vil- lage,
3. Sing then of Da- vid's Son, our Sav- ior and broth- er;
4. He gave his life for us, the pledge of sal- va- tion,
5. He con- quered sin and death; he tru- ly has ris- en.

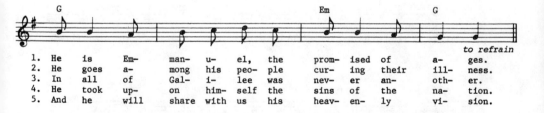

to refrain

1. He is Em- man- u- el, the prom- ised of a- ges.
2. He goes a- mong his peo- ple cur- ing their ill- ness.
3. In all of Gal- i- lee was nev- er an- oth- er.
4. He took up- on him- self the sins of the na- tion.
5. And he will share with us his heav- en- ly vi- sion.

50 King of Kings

Words and Music by
Charles Christmas

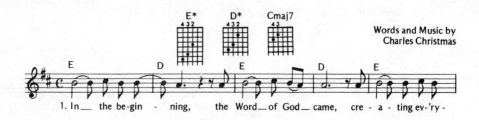

1. In the be-gin - ning, the Word of God came, cre - a - ting ev - 'ry -

thing by call - ing its name. "Let there be light, and call it the

day. Let there be night. Oh hear and o - bey."

REFRAIN

He's the King of Kings. He's the Lord of Lords. He's the

mas - ter of ev - 'ry - thing. Let Him be a - dored. *to verse*

2. And the Word, He made man as the crown of cre - a - tion, but man, he

fell in - to sin and sep - a - ra tion. So the Word be - came flesh in

space___ and___ time, bring-ing sal - va - tion to all___ man - kind.

to refrain

3. Oh, Je - sus, you are the lov-ing Sav - ior. Je -

sus, you are the way for us. Oh, wor-ship the King for there

is___ no___ oth - er.___ To Him___ sing; He's your Lord ___ and broth - er.

to refrain

After the final verse, the refrain may be repeated using the words "You're the King of Kings.
You're the Lord of Lords. You're the master of everything. May you be adored."

Let All That Is Within Me   51

Translation by
Melvin Harrel

Composer Unknown

Let all that is with-in me___ cry, "Ho-ly!" Let all that is with-in me___ cry,

"Ho- ly!" Ho- ly! Ho- ly! Ho- ly is the Lamb that was slain.___

This song may be sung substituting "Worthy," "Jesus," or "Glory" for "Holy."

52 The Light of Christ

Words and Music by
Donald Fishel

REFRAIN

The light of Christ has come in-to the world, the

The light of Christ has come in-to the world,

light of Christ has come in-to the world.

the light of Christ has come.

Continued ➤

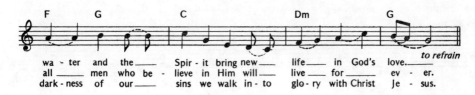

1. All men must be __ born a-gain to __ see the king-dom of God; __ the
2. God gave up His __ on-ly Son out of love __ for the __ world, __ so that
3. The light of God has __ come to us so that we might have sal - va-tion; from the

wa - ter and the __ Spir-it bring new __ life __ in God's love. __
all __ men who be - lieve in Him will __ live for __ ev - er.
dark-ness of our __ sins we walk in - to glo-ry with Christ Je - sus.

to refrain

Litany

53

Words and Music by
Rev. Carey Landry

REFRAIN

O Lord, our God, we lift up our hearts to you. O

Lord, our God, your peo-ple re - joice in you.

VERSE

God of the liv - ing. God of all peo - ple.

Fa - ther of life, we lift up our hearts to you.

Verses may be improvised using the above melody, as on album W/G 7302 from The Word of God.

54 The Lord Is My Light

Psalm 27:1

Music by
Pauline M. Mills

Capo 1, Play A

The Lord is my light___ and my___ sal- va- tion. Whom shall I

fear,___ Oh, Whom shall I fear?_ The Lord is my   fear,___ Whom shall I fear?___

The Lord is the strength,___ The strength of my life,_____ Of

Whom, then,___ shall I be a- fraid?_____ The Lord is my

The Lord Is Present in His Sanctuary 55

Words and Music by
Gail Cole

1. The Lord is pres-ent in His sanc-tu-ar- y, Let us praise the Lord! The
2. The Lord is pres-ent in His sanc-tu-ar- y, Let us sing to the Lord! The
3. The Lord is pres-ent in His sanc-tu-ar- y, Let us de-light in the Lord! The
4. The Lord is pres-ent in His sanc-tu-ar- y, Let us love the Lord! The

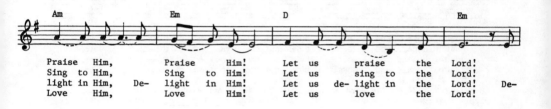

Lord is pres-ent in His peo- ple gath- ered here, Let us praise the Lord!
Lord is pres-ent in His peo- ple gath- ered here, Let us sing to the Lord!
Lord is pres-ent in His peo- ple gath- ered here, Let us de-light in the Lord! De-
Lord is pres-ent in His peo- ple gath- ered here, Let us love the Lord!

Praise Him, Praise Him! Let us praise the Lord!
Sing to Him, Sing to Him! Let us sing to the Lord!
light in Him, De- light in Him! Let us de- light in the Lord! De-
Love Him, Love Him! Let us love the Lord!

Praise Him, Praise Him! Let us praise Je- sus!
Sing to Him, Sing to Him! Let us sing to Je- sus!
light in Him, De- light in Him! Let us de-light in Je- sus!
Love Him, Love Him! Let us love Je- sus!

56 Love

I Cor. 13

Music by
Jean Goeboro

1. If I speak with the tongues of an-gels and men, if I
2. Love is pa-tient and kind, and bears all things; love does
3. Love is not jeal-ous, boast-ful, self-ish or rude; love
4. God is love, and he who lives in love lives in

have all pro-phet-ic pow'rs, if I have all faith but
not in-sist on its own way; love be-lieves all things; love
is not ir-ri-ta-ble; love does not re-joice at the
God and God in him. Je-sus is the Lord so

have not love, I am noth-ing at all. For
hopes all things; love en-dures all things. For
wrong, but right; love nev-er ends. For
let us love as He would have us do. For

faith, hope and love a-bide, but the great-est of these is love.
faith, hope and love a-bide, but the great-est of these is love.
faith, hope and love a-bide, but the great-est of these is love.
faith, hope and love a-bide, but the great-est of these is love.

57 The Love Round

Unknown

Love, love, love, love. Chris-tians, this is your call:

only on repeats

Love your neigh-bor as your-self, for God loves us all.

Optional verse: Jesus, Jesus, let me tell You how I feel:
You have given me Your riches; I love You so.

My Soul Doth Magnify the Lord   58

Luke 1: 46, 47, 49

Unknown

My soul doth mag-ni-fy the Lord, and my spir-it hath re-joiced in God my

Sa-vior, for___ He that is might-y hath done great things; and

ho-ly is His name. My soul doth mag-ni-fy the Lord, my soul doth

mag-ni-fy the Lord, and my spir-it hath re-joiced in God my Sa-vior, for___

He that is might-y hath done great things; and ho-ly is His name.

O Come, Let Us Adore Him   59

Latin, 18th c.
Tr. by Fr. Oakeley (1802–1880)
(and others)

Adeste Fidelis
Cantus Diversi by
J. F. Wade (1710–1786)

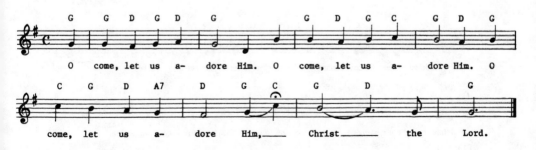

O come, let us a-dore Him. O come, let us a-dore Him. O

come, let us a-dore Him,___ Christ___ the Lord.

The following verses, or spontaneous verses, may also be used.

For He alone is worthy.
And He shall come in glory.

60 Praise My God With the Tambourine

First Chorus in Unison; others in parts.

Boldly, with vigor
Chorus

Words and Music by
Diane Davis

Praise my God with the tam-bou-rine; sing to the Lord with the cym-bals. bals.

Last time only Verse

MEN: 1. I will sing a **new** song to my God. "You are great, You are glo-ri-ous, won-der-ful-ly strong." *To Chorus*

WOMEN: 2. "May your whole cre-a-tion serve you. When you speak, things come in-to being; no one can re-sist your voice."

ALL: 3. "Should the moun-tains top-ple to min-gle with the waves, should rocks melt like wax be-fore your face, to those who fear you, you would still be mer-ci-ful." *To Chorus*

61 Psalm 89

Words and Music by
Karen Barrie

1. I have made a cov-e-nant with my cho-sen, giv-en my ser-vant my word.

I have made your name to last for-ev-er, built to out-last all time.

REFRAIN

I will cel-e-brate your love for-ev-er, Yah-weh. Age on age, my

Psalm 145

Words and Music by
Charles Christmas

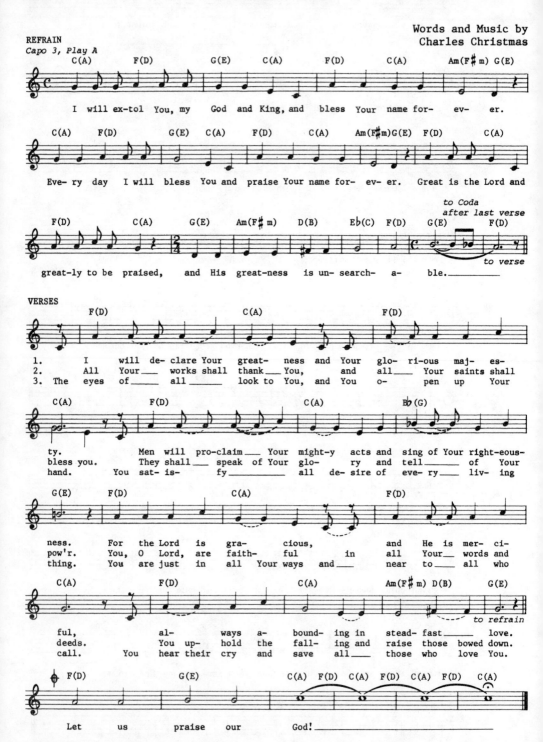

REFRAIN
Capo 3, Play A

I will ex-tol You, my God and King, and bless Your name for- ev- er.

Eve- ry day I will bless You and praise Your name for- ev- er. Great is the Lord and

to Coda
after last verse

to verse

great-ly to be praised, and His great-ness is un- search- a- ble._____

VERSES

1. I will de-clare Your great- ness and Your glo- ri-ous maj- es-
2. All Your___ works shall thank___ You, and all___ Your saints shall
3. The eyes of___ all___ look to You, and You o- pen up Your

ty. Men will pro-claim___ Your might-y acts and sing of Your right-eous-
bless you. They shall___ speak of Your glo- ry and tell___ of Your
hand. You sat-is- fy_____ all de-sire of ev- ry liv- ing

ness. For the Lord is gra- cious, and He is mer- ci-
pow'r. You, O Lord, are faith- ful in all Your___ words and
thing. You are just in all Your ways and___ near to___ all who

ful, al- ways a- bound- ing in stead-fast___ love.
deeds. You up-hold the fall- ing and raise those bowed down.
call. You hear their cry and save all___ those who love You.

to refrain

Let us praise our God!_____

Rejoice Always

I Thes. 5:16-18

Music by
Tom and Ellen Gryniewicz

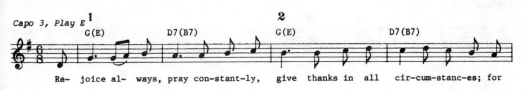

Re- joice al- ways, pray con-stant-ly, give thanks in all cir-cum-stanc-es; for

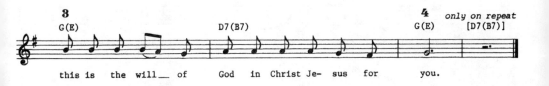

this is the will__ of God in Christ Je- sus for you.

Rejoice in the Lord Always

Philippians 4:4

by Evelyn Tarner

Re- joice in the Lord__ al- ways, and a- gain I say, "Re- joice!"

Re- joice! Re- joice! And a- gain I say, "Re- joice!"

65 Romans Eight

Words by E. Garzilli
Based on Romans 8:28-38

Music by
Enrico Garzilli

REFRAIN

For to those who love God, who are called in His plan, eve-ry-

thing works out for good. And God Him- self chose

them to bear the like- ness of His Son, that He might be the first of

man-y, man-y broth-ers. *to verse* broth- ers.

VERSES

1. Who is a- ble to con- demn? On- ly Christ who died for

us; Christ who rose for us; Christ who prays for us. *to refrain*

2. In the face of all this, what is there left to

say? For if God is for us, who can be a-gainst us? *to refrain*

3. Who can sep- a- rate us from the love of

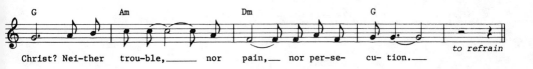

Christ? Nei-ther trou-ble,_____ nor pain,__ nor per-se- cu- tion.__ *to refrain*

4. .What can sep- a- rate us from the love of Christ? Not the

past, the pres- ent, nor the fu- ture.____ *to refrain*

66 Seek Ye First/Matt. 6:33

Music by
Karen Lafferty

1. Seek ___ ye first the ___ king - dom of God and His ___ right - eous - ness, ___
2. Ask and it shall be ___ giv - en un - to you; seek and ___ ye shall ___ find; ___

Al - le - lu - ia. Al - le - lu - ia.

and all these things shall be add - ed un - to you. Al - le - lu, Al-le - lu - ia.
knock and it shall be ___ o - pened un - to you. Al - le - lu, Al-le - lu - ia.

Al - le - lu - ia. Al - le - lu - ia.

The second verse included here is not part of "Seek Ye First" as written by Karen Lafferty.
Its origin is unknown.

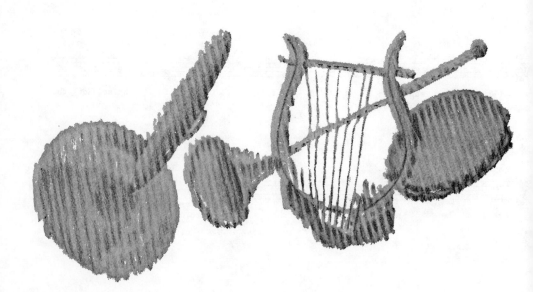

Based on Psalm 149, P.Q.   Paul Quinlan

Sing to God a brand new, brand new can-ti-cle and

fill the val-leys with a new song, Fill the val-leys,

yes, and go fill the cit-ies too, and Sing the

an-cient al-le-lu. Is-ra-el let your joy
For the Lord is a God
For the Lord is a King

be God and sing: Praise the Lord in ev-'ry thing,
of love, Come to free all the poor with vic-to-ry,
of kings, God on high in whose love we'll nev-er die,

Al-le-lu-ia, praise the Lord, and let the

na-tions, shout, and clap their hands for joy.

Let the na-tions shout and clap their hands for

joy.   joy.

68 Sing to the Lord

Words and Music by
Donald Fishel

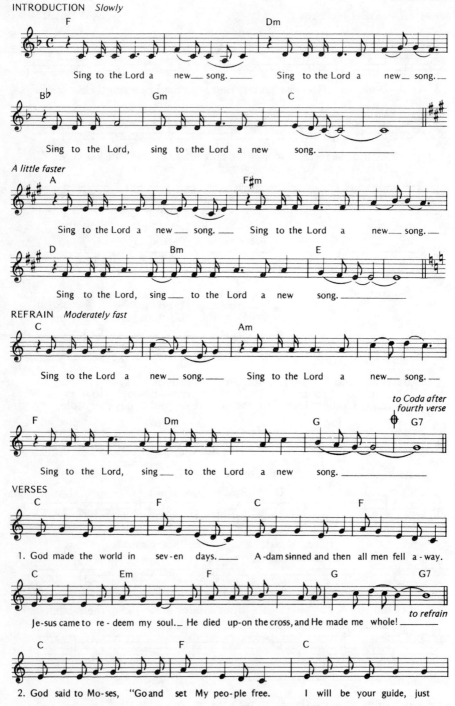

INTRODUCTION *Slowly*

F ... Dm

Sing to the Lord a new song. Sing to the Lord a new song.

Bb ... Gm ... C

Sing to the Lord, sing to the Lord a new song.

A little faster

A ... F#m

Sing to the Lord a new song. Sing to the Lord a new song.

D ... Bm ... E

Sing to the Lord, sing to the Lord a new song.

REFRAIN *Moderately fast*

C ... Am

Sing to the Lord a new song. Sing to the Lord a new song.

to Coda after fourth verse

F ... Dm ... G ... G7

Sing to the Lord, sing to the Lord a new song.

VERSES

C ... F ... C ... F

1. God made the world in sev-en days. A-dam sinned and then all men fell a-way.

C ... Em ... F ... G ... G7

to refrain

Je-sus came to re-deem my soul. He died up-on the cross, and He made me whole!

C ... F ... C

2. God said to Mo-ses, "Go and set My peo-ple free. I will be your guide, just

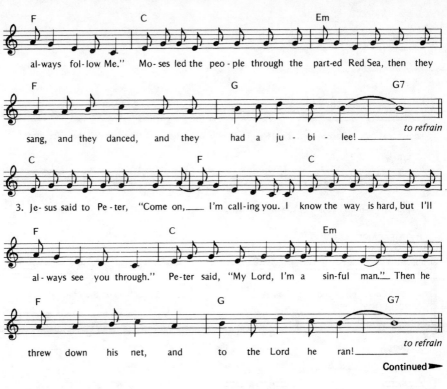

F   **C**   **Em**

al - ways fol - low Me." Mo - ses led the peo - ple through the part-ed Red Sea, then they

F   **G**   **G7**

sang, and they danced, and they had a ju - bi - lee! _____

to refrain

C   **F**   **C**

3. Je - sus said to Pe - ter, "Come on, ____ I'm call-ing you. I know the way is hard, but I'll

F   **C**   **Em**

al - ways see you through." Pe - ter said, "My Lord, I'm a sin-ful man." Then he

F   **G**   **G7**

threw down his net, and to the Lord he ran! ____

to refrain

Continued ▶

Song of Good News

Words by
Fr. Willard Jabusch

Israeli Folk Melody

VERSES

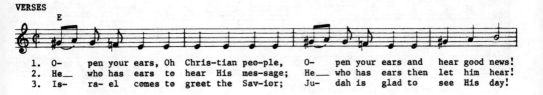

1. O- pen your ears, Oh Chris-tian peo-ple, O- pen your ears and hear good news!
2. He— who has ears to hear His mes-sage; He— who has ears then let him hear!
3. Is- ra- el comes to greet the Sav-ior; Ju- dah is glad to see His day!

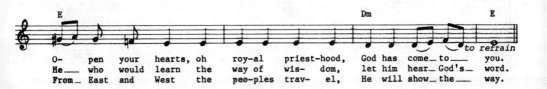

to refrain

O- pen your hearts, oh roy-al priest-hood, God has come to— you.
He— who would learn the way of wis- dom, let him hear— God's— word.
From— East and West the peo-ples trav- el, He will show— the— way.

REFRAIN

God has spo- ken to His peo- ple, Hal- le- lu- jah!

to verse

And His words are words of wis- dom, Hal- le- lu- jah!

70 The Song of Moses

Words by B. C. Pulkingham
Based on Exodus 15

Words and Music by
Betty Carr Pulkingham

REFRAIN
Capo 2, Play Am
DESCANT *only after fourth verse*

Lord is my strength and song, and He is be-come__ my sal-

MELODY
The Lord__ is my strength and__ song, and He is be-come__ my sal-

va-tion. He is my God and I will pre-pare Him an

va-tion. He is my God and I will pre-pare Him an

hab-i-ta-tion, my__ fa-ther's God and I will ex-alt Him.

hab-i-ta-tion, my__ fa-ther's God and I will ex-alt Him.
to verse

1. He hath tri-umphed glo-rious-ly,__ I will sing un-to the Lord. He hath tri-umphed

glo-rious-ly, the horse and his ri-der hath He thrown in the sea.__
to refrain

2. The Lord__ is a man of war, the Lord__ is His name. Pha-roh's char-iots

and his host hath He · cast, hath He cast in-to the sea!
to refrain

Em(Dm)   Bm(Am)

3. Thy right hand, O Lord, is be— come glo— ri— ous in   pow'r.

Em(Dm)   Bm(Am)   F♯7(E7)

Thy right hand, O   Lord,   hath cast in piec— es   the en— e— my.

to refrain

Em(Dm)   Bm(Am)   Em(Dm)

4. Who is like un—to Thee, O   Lord,__ a— mong the   gods? Who is like Thee,

Em(Dm)   Bm(Am)   F♯7(E7)

D.S. al Coda

glo—rious in ho— li—ness, fear—ful in prais— es,   do— ing won— ders? The

Continued ➤

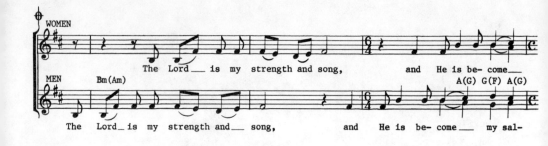

WOMEN

The Lord__ is my strength and song, and He is be-come__

MEN

Bm(Am) A(G) G(F) A(G)

The Lord__ is my strength and__ song, and He is be-come__ my sal-

my sal- va- tion.__ He is my God and I will pre-

Bm(Am)

va-tion. He is my God and I will pre- pare__ Him an

pare__ Him an hab- i- ta- tion, my__ fa- ther's God and

Bm(Am) Em(Dm) F#m(Em)

hab- i- ta- tion, my__ fa- ther's God and I will ex-

I will ex- alt Him. I__ will ex- alt Him!

Bm(Am) Em(Dm) Bm(Am)

alt Him. I__ will ex- alt Him!

The Spirit and the Bride 71

Based on Revelation 22:12–17

Words and Music by
Charles Christmas

REFRAIN

The Spir-it and the bride_ say, "Come." Let all who hear_ say, "Come." Let

to Coda
after last verse

him who is thirst-y come take the wa- ter of life with-out price._

to verse

VERSES

1. Be- hold, I am_ com- ing soon bring-ing_ my re-
2. Blessed_ are all who_ wash their robes to eat_ from the tree of
3. If an- y man thirst, let him come to me, and_ let him

ward. I_ am the Al- pha and_ the O-
life, and en- ter the cit- y by the gates. I_ am the
drink, and out of his heart there shall flow streams of liv- ing

me- ga, the first and the last, the be- gin- ing and_ the end._
off-spring of Da- vid, the_ bright and morn-ing star._
wa- ter. This is the Spir- it; just_ ask_ and_ re- ceive._

to refrain

E- ven so, come, Lord Je-sus! Come, Lord Je- sus!_

72 The Spirit Is A-Movin'

Words and Music by
Carey Landry
Pentecost, 1967

Quick tempo, but steady.

THE SPI-RIT IS A—MOV-IN' ALL O—VER, ALL O—VER THIS LAND.

1. PEO-PLE ARE GATH-ER-IN', THE CHURCH IS BORN, THE

SPI-RIT IS A-BLOW-IN' ON A WORLD RE—BORN.

2. Doors are opening as the Spirit comes,
   His fire is burning in his people now.

3. Filled with the Spirit we are sent to serve,
   We are called out as brothers, we are called to work.

4. The world, born once, is born again,
   We re-create it in love and joy.

5. Old men are dreaming dreams,
   And young men see the light.

6. Old walls are falling down,
   And men are speaking with each other.

7. The Spirit fills us with his power
   To be his witnesses to all we meet.

8. The Spirit urges us to travel light
   To be men of courage who spread his fire.

9. God has poured out his Spirit
   On all—on all of mankind.

Spirit of the Living God   73

Adapted from "Spirit Of the Living God"
Words and Music by
Daniel Iverson

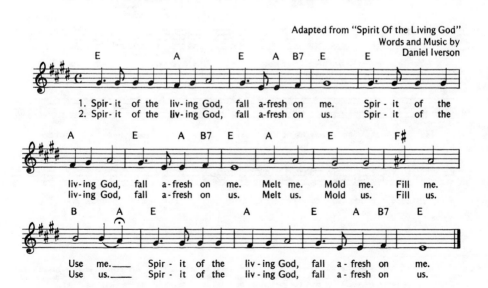

1. Spir-it of the liv-ing God, fall a-fresh on me. Spir-it of the liv-ing God, fall a-fresh on me. Melt me. Mold me. Fill me. Use me.___ Spir-it of the liv-ing God, fall a-fresh on me.

2. Spir-it of the liv-ing God, fall a-fresh on us. Spir-it of the liv-ing God, fall a-fresh on us. Melt us. Mold us. Fill us. Use us.___ Spir-it of the liv-ing God, fall a-fresh on us.

74 There Is None Like Him

C.J.R.

Clarence Jos. Rivers

Capo 1, Play E

4 He was born of a Vir-gin, And He lived as a com-mon man, Yet none the less our God, O there is none like Him.

5 He was the God im-mor-tal, Yet He died up-on a cross, And in dy-ing He slew death. O there is none like Him.

6 He was the Lord al-might-y, Yet He did not use His pow-er, And His weak-ness was like strength. O there is none like Him.

7 He lived with us, He died for us, He made Him-self our food, We are mem-bers of His Bo-dy. There is none like Him.

75 There's a River of Life

Verses two through six by
Betty Carr Pulkingham

Music and verse one by
L. Casebolt

There's a riv-er of life flow-ing out through me. It makes the lame to

walk and the blind to see. O-pens pris-on doors, sets the cap-tives

free. There's a riv-er of life flow-ing out through me.

2. There's a fountain flowing from the Savior's side,
   All my sins forgiven in that precious tide,
   Jesus paid the price when for me He died.
   There's a fountain flowing from the Savior's side.

3. There's a risen Savior at the Father's throne,
   Ever interceding for His very own,
   Pouring down the blessings that are His alone.
   There's a risen Savior at the Father's throne.

4. There's a Holy Comforter who's sent from Heaven,
   All the glorious gifts are His, and have been given,
   He'll show us more of Jesus 'til the veil is riven.
   There's a Holy Comforter who's sent from Heaven.

5. There's a land of rest that we may enter now,
   Freed from all our works and freed from Satan's power,
   Just resting in the Lord each moment and each hour.
   There's a land of rest that we may enter now.

6. There's a full salvation wrought for you and me,
   From faith to faith and glory to glory eternally,
   O Lord, just take this life and let me live for Thee.
   There's a full salvation wrought for you and me.

They That Wait Upon the Lord

76

Based on Isaiah 40:31

Words and Music by
Stuart Hamblen

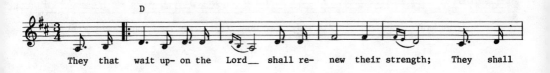

They that wait up- on the Lord__ shall re- new their strength; They shall

mount up with wings____ as ea- gles;____ They shall run and not be

wea- ry; They shall walk and not__ faint; Teach me, Lord, Teach me,

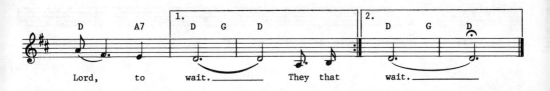

1.
Lord, to wait._____ They that

2.
wait._____

This Is the Day

Psalm 118:24

Unknown

This is the day, this is the day that the Lord has made, that the

Lord has made. Let us re-joice, let us re-joice and be

glad in it, and be glad in it. This is the day that the Lord has made.
Let us re-joice and be glad in it.

This is the day, this is the day that the Lord has made.

We See the Lord

Verses two, three, and four by
James E. Byrne

Unknown

1. We see the Lord, we see the Lord, and He is
2. We see the Lord, we see the Lord, and His
3. We hear the Lord, we hear the Lord, and His
4. We bless the Lord, we bless the Lord, and as

high and lift-ed up, and His train fills the Tem-ple, He is
face___ shines___ forth as a light in the Tem-ple, and His
Word is-sues forth and re-sounds through the Tem-ple, and His
in-cense goes up, so our prayers fill the Tem-ple, and as

high and lift-ed up, and His train fills the Tem-ple. The
face___ shines___ forth as a light in the Tem-ple. The
Word___ is-sues forth and re-sounds through the Tem-ple. The
in-cense goes up, so our prayers fill the Tem-ple. The

an-gels cry, "Ho-ly." The an-gels cry, "Ho-ly." The
ser-aphs cry, "Worth-y." The ser-aphs cry, "Worth-y." The
el-ders cry, "A-men." The el-ders cry, "A-men." The
peo-ple cry, "Glo-ry." The peo-ple cry, "Glo-ry." The

an-gels cry "Ho-ly is the Lord!"
ser-aphs cry "Worth-y is the Lord!"
el-ders cry "A-men! It is so!"
peo-ple cry "Glo-ry to the Lord!"

79 When the Spirit Moves You

Words and Music by
Michael Fitzgerald

REFRAIN

When the Spir- it moves you, lord, you've got to move.

When the Spir- it moves you, lord, you've got to move.

When the Spir- it moves you, lord, good broth- er, you've got to o- pen up your heart and lis- ten to Him. When the Spir- it moves you, lord, you've got to move. *to verse*

VERSES

1. Now the Lord said to A- bra- ham, "Lead my peo- ple there, From the land that you're set- tling to the land of Ca- naan." Now A- bra- ham said to the Lord, "An- y- thing You want to ask of me." When the Spir- it moves you, lord, you've got to move. *to refrain*

2. Now the Lord said to Mos- es, "Lead my peo- ple free, From the land of the Pha- roah to the prom- ised land." Now Mos- es said to the Lord, "An- y- thing You want to ask of me." When the Spir- it moves you, lord, you've got to move. *to refrain*

3. Now lis- ten here, peo- ple_____ to what I've got to___ say.___ When the

Lord speaks to us, we have to an- swer this way:___ We've got to

o- pen up our hearts to His love_____ and hear His words of Truth.__

_____ When the Spir-it moves you, lord, you've got to move.___ *to refrain*

Alabaré

Unknown

Copyright unknown

án.   Y es-os mon-tes se mo-ver-án.   Y es-os
moved.   And e-ven moun-tains___ shall be moved.   And e-ven

mon-tes se mo-ver-án.   Más con su San-to Es pír-i-tu.   *to refrain*
moun-tains___ shall be moved.   By the Ho-ly Spir-it's power.

The following section may be sung several times, using the names of different countries.

Y Puer-to Ri-co se sal-va rá.   Y Puer-to Ri-co se sal-va
And Puer-to Ri-co___ shall be saved.   And Puer-to Ri-co___ shall be

rá.   Y Puer-to Ri-co se sal-va rá.   Más con su
saved.   And Puer-to Ri-co___ shall be saved.   By the

San-to Es-pír-i-tu.   **1.** Y (tam-bien) tu.   **2.** *to refrain*
Ho-ly Spir-it's power.   And (al-so) power.

202   All of My Life

Words and Music by
Germaine Kramlinger

REFRAIN

All of___ my life   I will___ sing praise to my

God.___

VERSES

1. For cre-a-tion, praise; For sal-va-tion___ praise;   For all man-kind, praise.   *to refrain*
2. For the Vir-gin, praise; For the saints and an-gels praise;   For the Church,___ praise.

3. To the Fa-ther, praise; To the Son, sing praise;   To the Spir-it, praise.   *to refrain*

Alleluia, Sing to Jesus

203

Words by
William C. Dix

Music by
R. H. Prichard

Capo 3, Play D

1. Al - le - lu - ia! sing— to Je - sus! His— the— scep - ter, His— the throne;
2. Al - le - lu - ia! not— as or - phans are— we— left— in sor - row now;
3. Al - le - lu - ia! Bread— of Heav - en, Thou— on— earth— our food,— our stay!

Al - le - lu - ia! His— the tri - umph, His— the— vic - to - ry— a - lone;
Al - le - lu - ia! He— is near— us, Faith— be - lieves, nor ques - tions how:
Al - le - lu - ia! here— the sin - ful flee— to— Thee from day— to day;

Hark! the songs— of peace - ful Zi - on thun - der like— a might - y flood;—
Though the cloud— from sight re - ceived— Him when— the for - ty days— were o'er,—
In - ter - ces - sor, friend— of sin - ners, earth's Re - deem - er, plead— for me,—

Je - sus out— of eve - ry na - tion— hath re - deemed— us by His blood.
Shall— our hearts for - get— His prom - ise, "I— am with— you ev - er - more"?
Where— the songs— of all— the sin - less sweep— a - cross the crys - tal sea.

204 Amazing Grace

Words and Music by
John Newton

1. A - maz - ing _ grace, how sweet _ the sound that saved _ a _ wretch _ like me!
2. 'Twas grace _ that _ taught my heart _ to fear, and grace _ my _ fears _ re - lieved;
3. Through man - y _ dan - gers, toils, _ and snares, I have _ al - read - y come;
4. The Lord _ has prom - ised good _ to me, His word _ my _ hope _ se - cures;
5. And when _ this _ flesh and heart _ shall fail, and mor - tal _ life _ shall cease;
6. When we've _ been _ there ten thou - sand years, bright shin - ing _ as _ the sun,

_ I once _ was _ lost, _ but now _ am _ found, was blind, but now _ I _ see. _
_ How pre - cious _ did _ that grace _ ap - pear the hour _ I _ first _ be - lieved!
_ 'Tis grace _ has brought _ me safe _ thus _ far, and grace _ will _ lead _ me home.
_ He will _ my _ shield _ and por - tion _ be as long _ as _ life _ en - dures.
_ I shall _ pos - sess, _ with - in _ the _ veil, a life _ of _ joy _ and peace.
_ We've no _ less _ days _ to sing _ God's _ praise than when _ we'd _ first _ be - gun.

205 Amen, Our Hearts Cry

Words and Music by
John C. Blattner

Based on Ex. 19:8

G#7*
(F#7*)

REFRAIN
Capo 2, Play Bm

A - men, a - men our hearts _ cry, His word is true. All that the Lord has said _ we will do. _

VERSES

F#m(Em)   C#m(Bm)   F#m(Em)   C#m(Bm)

1. You have borne us on eag - les' wings; we have wit-nessed Your power.

A(G)   E(D)   F#(E)   G#(F#) (F#7*)(F#7)   G#7* G#7

Yah-weh, You will be our Lord; Your word will be our law. *to refrain*

F#m(Em)   C#m(Bm)   F#m(Em)   C#m(Bm)

2. The One who called forth cre - a - tion, who raised up man-kind from dust,

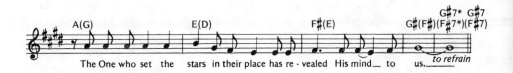

A(G)   E(D)   F#(E)   G#(F#)(F#7*)(F#7)   G#7* G#7

The One who set the stars in their place has re - vealed His mind to us. *to refrain*

F#m(Em)   C#m(Bm)   F#m(Em)   C#m(Bm)

3. He has not spo-ken in se - cret, or in some dark - ened land.

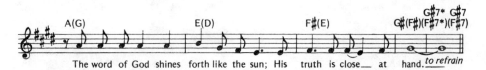

A(G)   E(D)   F#(E)   G#(F#)(F#7*)(F#7)   G#7* G#7

The word of God shines forth like the sun; His truth is close at hand. *to refrain*

F#m(Em)   C#m(Bm)   F#m(Em)   C#m(Bm)

4. "See the first things have come to pass; all that I spoke has come true.

A(G)   E(D)   F#(E)   G#(F#)(F#7*)(F#7)   G#7* G#7

Be-fore a new thing breaks from the bud, I de-clare it to you." *to refrain*

206 As a Doe

Psalm 42 adapted by
Michael Fitzgerald

Music by
Michael Fitzgerald

REFRAIN

As a doe longs___ for run-ning streams, so longs my
soul for___ You, my God._____

VERSES

1. My soul is thirst - ing for the God of life. When shall I
3. Why so down - cast,_____ O my soul? Why do you
5. May Yah - weh com - mand His___ love at dawn, and by night
7. Why so down - cast,_____ O my soul? Why do you

see Him_____ face to face? I have no food but___
sigh_____ deep with - in? Put___ your hope in the
may___ I sing Him a song. Let___ me sing to___
melt_____ deep with - in? Put___ your hope in the

tears	day and	night,___	and men say, "Where is your God?"___
God___	of	life.	I___ shall praise Him a - gain.___
God___	my	ref - uge,	"Why do you for - get___ me?"___
God___	of	life,___	and I shall praise Him a - gain.___

2. I___ re - mem - ber___ and my soul melts with - in. I'm on my
4. When I find my soul___ down - cast with - in. I think of
6. Why must I walk___ op - pressed by the foe, all___ my
8. Glo - ry be___ to God the Fa - - ther, and___ to

way to the house___ of God, a - mong cries___ of
you, O Mount Zi - - on. Deep calls to deep as your
bones near - ly bro - ken with - in, as all day men___ say,
Je - sus the Lord,___ and to the Ho - ly

joy___ and praise. Place___ your trust___ in God.___
wa - ters roar. O - ver me all your waves pour.___
"Where is your God?" But I shall praise Him a - gain.___
Spir - - it. I will sing praise ev - er - more.___

to refrain

Blessed Be the Name

207

Words by
William H. Clark

Music by
Ralph E. Hudson

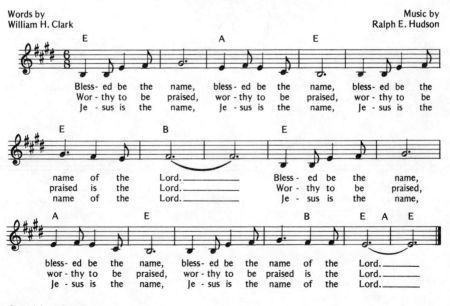

Bless- ed be the	name,	bless- ed be the	name, bless- ed be the
Wor - thy to be	praised,	wor - thy to be	praised, wor - thy to be
Je - sus is the	name,	Je - sus is the	name, Je - sus is the

name of the Lord.___ Bless - ed be the name,
praised is the Lord.___ Wor - thy to be praised,
name of the Lord.___ Je - sus is the name,

bless- ed be the name, bless- ed be the name of the Lord.___
wor - thy to be praised, wor - thy to be praised is the Lord.___
Je - sus is the name, Je - sus is the name of the Lord.___

208 From Heaven the Lord Looks Down

Psalm 45:1

Words and Music by
Leo Nestor

1. From heav'n the Lord____ looks down____ up-on the chil-dren of men,____ to see if there____ be one who does good,____ and keeps____ the law in his heart.

2. Our hearts are rest - less for Thee,____ and rest - less al - ways shall be____ un - til they drink of the springs of Your love,____ and rise____ rest - less no more.____

3. How love - ly is____ this place,____ the dwell - ing place of the Lord.____ My heart and soul____ have yearned____ and pined____ for God, the liv - ing God.

REFRAIN

My heart____ o - ver - flows.____ I sing____ my ode____ to the King.____ My tongue flows like the pen of a scribe. I sing____ the praise of the Lord. Ooh.____

Glorify Thy Name

209

Words and Music by
Donna Adkins

Fa - ther, we love Thee, we praise Thee, we a - dore Thee. Glo - ri-fy Thy
Je - sus, we love Thee, we praise Thee, we a - dore Thee. Glo - ri-fy Thy
Spir - it, we love Thee, we praise Thee, we a - dore Thee. Glo - ri-fy Thy

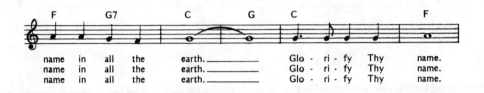

name in all the earth. _____ Glo - ri - fy Thy name.
name in all the earth. _____ Glo - ri - fy Thy name.
name in all the earth. _____ Glo - ri - fy Thy name.

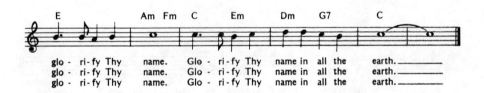

glo - ri-fy Thy name. Glo - ri-fy Thy name in all the earth. _____
glo - ri-fy Thy name. Glo - ri-fy Thy name in all the earth. _____
glo - ri-fy Thy name. Glo - ri-fy Thy name in all the earth. _____

210 Grant to Us

Ez. 36:26 and Jer. 31:31-34 adapted by
Lucien Deiss, C.S.Sp.

Music by
Lucien Deiss, C.S.Sp.

REFRAIN

Grant to us, O Lord, a heart re-newed. Re-cre-ate in us Your own Spir-it, Lord!

VERSES

1. Be-hold, the days are com-ing, says the Lord our God, when I will

make a new cov-e-nant with the house of Is-ra-el. *to refrain*

2. Deep with-in their be-ing I will im-plant my law; I will write it in their hearts. *to refrain*

3. I will be their God, and they shall be my peo-ple. *to refrain*

4. And for all their faults I will grant for-give-ness; nev-er-more will I re-mem-ber their sins. *to refrain*

Hallelujah, My Father

211

Words and Music by
Tim Cullen

Hal - le - lu - jah,— my Fa - ther, for— giv-ing us Your Son, send - ing Him in - to the world to be giv-en up for man, Know-ing— we would bruise Him— and smite Him from— the— earth.— Hal - le - lu - jah,— my— Fa - ther,— in His death— is my birth. Hal - le - lu - jah,— my— Fa - ther,— in His life— is my life.——

212 Hallelujah, Our God Reigns

Revelation 19:6-7

Words and Music by
Dale Garratt

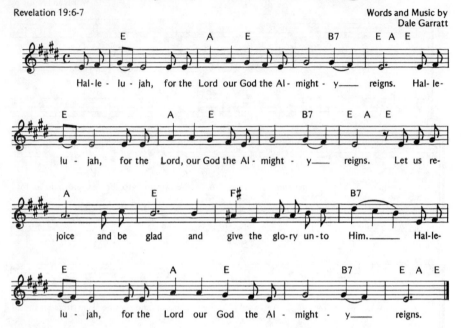

Hal-le - lu - jah, for the Lord our God the Al - might - y___ reigns. Hal-le-

lu - jah, for the Lord, our God the Al - might - y___ reigns. Let us re-

joice and be glad and give the glo-ry un-to Him.___ Hal-le-

lu - jah, for the Lord our God the Al - might - y___ reigns.

Holy God, We Praise Thy Name   213

Ascribed to St. Nicetas
Tr. C. Walworth
Capo 3, Play D

Arranged by
Kalman Antos

1. Ho-ly God,___ we praise___ Thy___ Name! Lord of all___ we
2. Hark! the loud___ ce-les-tial___ hymn An-gel choirs a-

bow___ be-fore Thee; All on earth___ Thy scep-tre___ claim,
bove___ are rais-ing; Cher-u-bim___ and Ser-a-phim

All in heav'n___ a-bove___ a-dore Thee: In-fi-nite___ Thy
In un-ceas-ing cho-rus prais-ing; Fill___ the___ heav'ns___ with

vast___ do-main,___ Ev-er-last-ing is___ Thy reign. reign.
sweet___ ac-cord; Ho-ly, Ho-ly, Ho-ly Lord! Lord!

214 The Horse and Rider

Words anonymous
Exodus 15:1

Music by I. Miron and J. Grossman

I will sing un - to the Lord, for He has tri-umphed glo-rious - ly; the

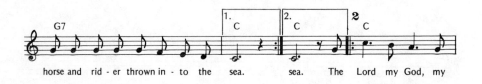

horse and rid - er thrown in - to the sea.   sea.   The Lord my God, my

strength, my song, is now be-come my vic - to - ry.   The   ry.   The Lord is God and

I will praise Him, my fa-ther's God and I___ will ex-alt___Him. The   I___ will ex-alt Him.

This song is sometimes sung as a round. Numbers are included to indicate the three beginning points.

AFTER WILL JAMES

215   I Am the Resurrection

John 11:25-26

Words and Music by
Ray Repp

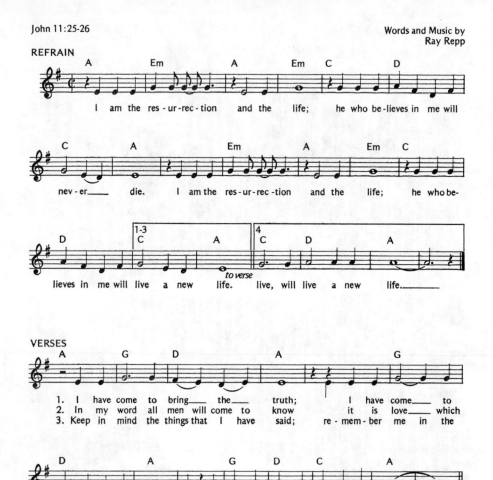

REFRAIN

I am the res-ur-rec-tion and the life; he who be-lieves in me will

nev-er___ die. I am the res-ur-rec-tion and the life; he who be-

lieves in me will live a new life. live, will live a new life.___

to verse

VERSES

1. I have come to bring___ the___ truth; I have come___ to
2. In my word all men will come to know it is love___ which
3. Keep in mind the things that I have said; re-mem-ber me in the

bring___ you___ life;___ if you be-lieve, then you shall___ live.___
makes the spir-it grow.___ if you be-lieve, then you shall___ live.___
break-ing of the bread.___ if you be-lieve, then you shall___ live.

to refrain

I Hear a Sound

Words and Music by
Himmie Gustafson

1. I hear a sound com-ing from the moun-tain, I hear it loud-er each day.
2. I see the King stand-ing on the moun-tain, I see Him clear-er each day.

I hear a sound com-ing from the moun-tain and it says, "Pre-pare ye the way." "Pre-
I see the King stand-ing on the moun-tain, and He says, "Pre-pare ye the way." "Pre-

pare ye the way, pre-pare ye the way, pre-pare ye the way of the Lord."
pare ye the way, pre-pare ye the way, pre-pare ye the way of the Lord."

217 Isaiah 60

Isaiah 60 adapted by
Donald Kopinski

Music by
Donald Kopinski

REFRAIN

A - rise, shine out, for your light has come. The glo - ry of

Yah-weh is ris-ing on you._____ Though night still cov-ers the earth, and

dark-ness the peo-ples,___ a - bove you, Yah-weh now ris - es; a - bove you His

glo-ry ap-pears; a - rise!_____ *to verse* rise!_____

VERSES

1. The na-tions come to Your light_ and kings to your dawn-ing bright-ness, sing-ing_ the

praise of Yah-weh,_ bring-ing gold_ and in-cense. Lift up your eyes and look a-round you;_

all are as-sem-bling and com-ing toward you. Your sons from far a - way,_ and your

daugh-ters be - ing ten-der-ly car-ried this day._____

to refrain

2. They bring your sons from far a-way and their sil-ver and gold with them. For the name of

Yah-weh, your God, the Ho-ly One of Is-ra-el._____ No more shall vio-lence be

heard in your coun-try, nor dev-a-sta-tion with-in your fron-tiers. You will call your

walls "Sal-va-tion,"_____ and your gates "Praise."_____

to refrain

3. No more will the sun give you day-light, nor moon-light shine on you._____ But

Yah-weh will be_____ your e-ter-nal light; your God will be your splen-dor. Your sun will

set no more,_____ nor your moon wane,_____ but Yah-weh will be your e-ter-nal light

and your days of mourn-ing will pass from your sight._____

to refrain

218   Jesus, I Love You

Words and Music by
Kathleen Thomerson

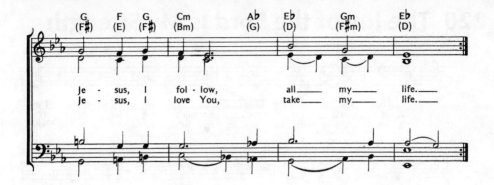

Je - sus, I fol - low, all___ my___ life.___
Je - sus, I love You, take___ my___ life.___

Joy Is the Flag

219

Unknown

Joy is the flag flown high from the cas - tle of my heart, from the

cas-tle of my heart, from the cas-tle of my heart. Joy is the flag flown high from the

cas-tle of my heart when the King is in res-i-dence there.__ So let it fly in the sky, let the

whole world know, let the whole world know, let the whole world know. So let it

fly in the sky, let the whole world know that the King is in res-i-dence there.__

220 The Joy of the Lord Is My Strength

Refrain, verses 1 and 3 by Alliene Vale
Verse 2 unknown

Music by Alliene G. Vale

1. The joy___ of the Lord___ is my strength. The
2. If you___ want___ joy___ you must sing for it. If
3. Ah— ha ha ha ha ha ha ha ha ha ha. Ah—

joy___ of the Lord___ is my strength. The joy___ of the Lord___
you___ want___ joy___ you must shout for it. If you___ want___ joy___ you must
— ha ha ha ha ha ha ha ha ha. Ah— ha ha ha ha ha ha ha

is my strength. The joy___ of the Lord___ is my strength.
jump for it. The joy___ of the Lord___ is my strength.
ha ha ha. The joy___ of the Lord___ is my strength.

221 Keep in Mind

II Tim. 2:8-11 adapted by
Lucien Deiss, C.S.Sp.

Music by
Lucien Deiss, C.S.Sp.

REFRAIN

Keep in mind that Je - sus Christ has died for us and is ris - en from the

dead. He is our sav - ing Lord, He is joy for all a - ges.

VERSES

1. If we die with the Lord, we shall live with the Lord.
2. If we en - dure with the Lord, we shall reign with the Lord.

to refrain

3. In Him all our sor - row, in Him all our joy.
4. In Him hope of glo - ry, in Him all our love.
5. In Him our re - demp - tion, in Him all our grace.
6. In Him our sal - va - tion, in Him all our peace.

to refrain

Let Trumpets Sound

222

Words by
Michael Cockett

Music by
Kevin Mayhew

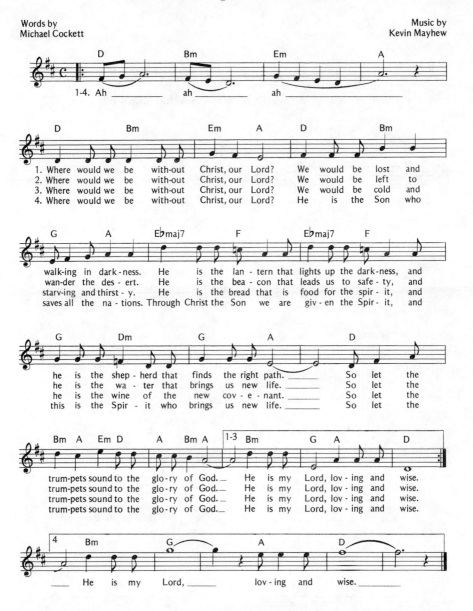

1-4. Ah ah ah

1. Where would we be with-out Christ, our Lord? We would be lost and
2. Where would we be with-out Christ, our Lord? We would be left to
3. Where would we be with-out Christ, our Lord? We would be cold and
4. Where would we be with-out Christ, our Lord? He is the Son who

walk-ing in dark-ness. He is the lan - tern that lights up the dark-ness, and
wan-der the des - ert. He is the bea - con that leads us to safe - ty, and
starv-ing and thirst - y. He is the bread that is food for the spir - it, and
saves all the na - tions. Through Christ the Son we are giv - en the Spir - it, and

he is the shep - herd that finds the right path. So let the
he is the wa - ter that brings us new life. So let the
he is the wine of the new cov - e - nant. So let the
this is the Spir - it who brings us new life. So let the

trum-pets sound to the glo-ry of God. He is my Lord, lov - ing and wise.
trum-pets sound to the glo-ry of God. He is my Lord, lov - ing and wise.
trum-pets sound to the glo-ry of God. He is my Lord, lov - ing and wise.
trum-pets sound to the glo-ry of God. He is my Lord, lov - ing and wise.

He is my Lord, lov - ing and wise.

223   Lift High the Banners of Love

Words and Music by
Rich Gillard

REFRAIN

Lift high the ban-ners of love, Hal-le - lu-jah. Sound the trum-pets of war.___

Christ has got-ten us the vic-t'ry, Hal-le - lu-jah. Jer - i - cho must ___ fall.___

VERSES

1. The bod - y of Christ is an ar - my, ___ fight - ing___
2. Broth-ers, are you sure of your call - ing, will you fight for___
3. We must___ stand in u - ni - ty, ___ by the___
4. Preach___ the___ Sav - ior___ cru - ci - fied, ___ dead, but
5. In the name___ of___ God the___ Fa - ther, in the name of___

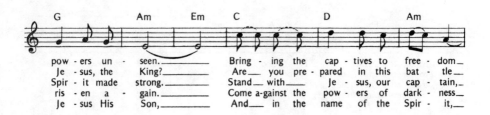

pow - ers un - seen. ___ Bring - ing the cap - tives to free - dom___
Je - sus, the King? ___ Are___ you pre - pared in this bat - tle
Spir - it made strong. ___ Stand___ with___ Je - sus, our cap - tain,
ris - en a - gain. ___ Come a-gainst the pow - ers of dark - ness
Je - sus His Son, ___ And___ in the name of the Spir - it, ___

___ in the name of ___ Je - sus, our King. ___
___ to lay down your lives for your friends? ___
___ and fight till God's king - dom has come. ___
___ in___ His glo - ri - ous name. ___
___ we will fight till___ we are called home. ___

to refrain

Look Beyond

224

Based on John 6

Words and Music by
Darryl Ducote

REFRAIN
Capo 3, Play D

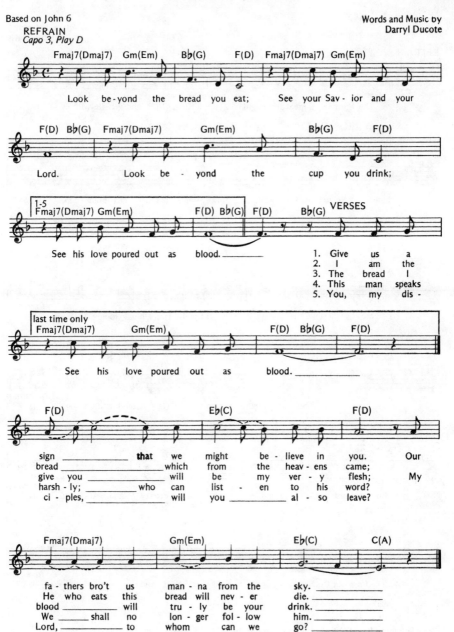

Look be-yond the bread you eat; See your Sav-ior and your Lord. Look be-yond the cup you drink;

See his love poured out as blood. _____

1. Give us a
2. I am the
3. The bread I
4. This man speaks
5. You, my dis -

last time only

See his love poured out as blood. _____

sign ____	**that**	we	might	be - lieve	in	you.	Our
bread ____	which	from	the	heav - ens	came;	Our
give you ____	will	be	my	ver - y	flesh;	My
harsh - ly; ____	who	can	list - en	to	his	word?
ci - ples, ____	will	you ____	al - so	leave?

fa - thers bro't	us	man - na	from the	sky. ____
He who eats	this	bread will	nev - er	die. ____
blood ____	will	tru - ly	be your	drink. ____
We ____ shall	no	lon - ger	fol - low	him. ____
Lord, ____	to	whom	can we	go? ____

225 The Lord Is a Great and Mighty King

Words and Music by
Diane Davis

REFRAIN

The Lord is a great and might - y King, just and gen-tle with ev - er - y-

thing. So with hap - pi - ness_____ we sing, and let His prais - es ring.

VERSES

1. We are His voice, we His song. Let us praise Him all day long. Al - le - lu - ia. *to refrain*

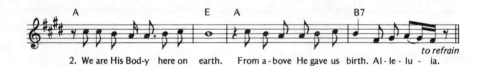

2. We are His Bod-y here on earth. From a - bove He gave us birth. Al - le - lu - ia. *to refrain*

3. For our Lord we will stand. sent by Him to ev-e - ry land. Al - le - lu - ia. *to refrain*

4. The Lord our God is __ one: Fa - ther, Spir - it and the Son. Al - le - lu - ia. *to refrain*

One Thing I Ask For

226

Based on Psalm 27

Words and Music by
Ted Kennedy III

REFRAIN

One thing I ask for, that shall I seek: to dwell in the house of the Lord.____ dwell in the house of the Lord.____ *to verse*

VERSES

1. All the days of my life, to be - hold___ the beau-ty of the Lord, and to in - quire in His tem - ple.____ *to refrain*

2. You've__ said__ to me,____ "Seek ye my face." My heart says, "Thy face do I seek!"____ *to refrain*
3. With__ all left be - hind, I seek on - ly God.___ Teach__ me Your ways,__ O God.____ *to refrain*
4. I will wait for the Lord, and He gives me strength.____ For__ I have seen__ His good - ness!____ *to Coda*

One thing I ask for, that shall I seek: to dwell in the house of the Lord.____ dwell in the house of the Lord.____ to dwell in the house of the Lord.____

227 Our God Reigns

Words adapted from Isaiah 52:7 and
Isaiah 53 by Leonard E. Smith, Jr.

Music by
Leonard E. Smith, Jr.

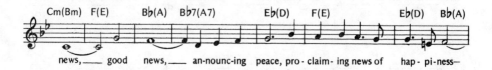

1. How lovely on the mountains are the feet of him
Who brings good news, good news,
Announcing peace, proclaiming news of happiness,
Saying to Zion: Your God reigns.
   Chorus Your God reigns. . . 4x

2. He had no stately form, he had no majesty,
That we should be drawn to him.
He was despised and we took no account of him
Yet now he reigns with the Most High.
   Chorus Now he reigns. . . 3x
   With the Most High.

3. It was our sin and guilt that bruised and wounded him,
It was our sin that brought him down.
When we like sheep had gone astray, our shepherd came
And on his shoulders bore our shame.
   Chorus On his shoulders. . . 3x
   He bore our shame.

4. Meek as a lamb that's led out to the slaughter-house,
Dumb as a sheep before it's shearer,
His life ran down upon the ground like pouring rain
That we might be born again.
   Chorus That we might be. . . 3x
   Born again.

5. Out from the tomb he came with grace and majesty,
He is alive—he is alive.
God loves us so—see here his hands, his feet, his side.
Yes, we know—he is alive.
   Chorus He is alive. . . 4x

6. How lovely on the mountains are the feet of him
Who brings good news, good news,
Announcing peace, proclaiming news of happiness:
Our God reigns—our God reigns.
   Chorus Our God reigns. . . 4x

Praise the Name of Jesus 228

Words and Music by
Roy Hicks, Jr.

Praise the name of Je - sus. Praise the name of Je - sus. He's my rock, He's my for-tress,

He's my de-liv-er-er, in Him will I trust. Praise the name of Je - sus.

229 The Prayer of St. Francis

Adapted by
Sebastian Temple

Music by
Sebastian Temple

1. Make me a chan-nel of Your peace. Where there is ha-tred, let me bring Your
2. Make me a chan-nel of Your peace. Where there's des-pair in life, let me bring

love. Where there is in-ju-ry, Your par-don, Lord, And
hope. Where there is dark-ness on-ly light, And

1.
where there's doubt, true faith in You. joy.

2.
where there's sad-ness ev-er joy. Oh,

Mas-ter, grant that I may nev-er seek so much to be con-soled as to con-

sole, to be un-der-stood as to un-der-stand, to be loved as to

love with all my soul. 3. Make me a chan-nel of Your

peace. It is in par-don-ing that we are par-doned, in giv-ing to all

men that we re-ceive, and in dy-ing that we're born to e-ter-nal life.

Priestly People

230

I Peter 2:9 adapted by
Lucien Deiss, C.S.Sp.

Music by
Lucien Deiss, C.S.Sp.

REFRAIN
Capo 2, Play G

Priest - ly peo - ple, King - ly peo - ple, Ho - ly peo - ple,

God's cho - sen peo - ple, Sing praise to the Lord.

VERSES

1. We sing to You, O Christ, be - lov - ed Son of the Fa - ther.
2. We sing to You, O Son,— born of Mar - y the Vir - gin.
3. We sing to You, O bright - ness of splen - dor and glo - ry.
4. We sing to You, O light— bring-ing men out of dark - ness.
5. We sing to You, Mes - si - ah fore-told by the proph - ets.

to refrain

We give You praise, O Wis - dom ev - er - last - ing, and Word of God.
We give You praise, Our Broth - er, born to heal us, Our sav - ing Lord.
We give You praise, O Morn - ing Star an - nounc - ing the com - ing day.
We give You praise, O guid - ing Light, who shows us the way to heaven.
We give You praise, O Son of Da - vid and Son of A - bra - ham.

6. We sing to You, Messiah, the hope of the people.
   We give You praise, O Christ, our Lord and King, humble, meek of heart.
7. We sing to You, The Way to the Father in heaven,
   We give You praise, The Way of Truth, and Way of all grace and light.
8. We sing to You, O Priest of the new dispensation,
   We give You praise, Our Peace, sealed by the blood of the Sacrifice.
9. We sing to You, O Lamb, put to death for the sinner,
   We give You praise, O Victim, immolated for all mankind.
10. We sing to You, The Tabernacle made by the Father,
    We give You praise, The Cornerstone and Savior of Israel.
11. We sing to You, The Shepherd who leads to the kingdom,
    We give You praise, Who gather all your sheep in the one true fold.
12. We sing to You, O Fount, overflowing with mercy.
    We give You praise, Who give us living waters to quench our thirst.
13. We sing to You, True Vine, planted by God our Father,
    We give You praise, O blessed Vine, whose branches bear fruit in love.
14. We sing to You, O Manna, which God gives his people.
    We give You praise, O living Bread, which comes down to us from heaven.
15. We sing to You, The Image of the Father eternal,
    We give You praise, O King of justice, Lord, and the King of peace.
16. We sing to You, The Firstborn of all God's creation,
    We give You praise, Salvation of your saints sleeping in the Lord.
17. We sing to You, O Lord, whom the Father exalted,
    We give You praise, In glory you are coming to judge all men.

231 Psalm 18

Psalm 18 adapted by
Jane Yankitis

Music by
Jane Yankitis

REFRAIN

Yea, Thou dost light my lamp; the Lord my God light-ens my dark-ness.

VERSES

1. Yea, by Thee I can crush a troop; and by Thee I can leap a wall. This God— His way is per-fect;— the prom-ise of the Lord proves true; He is my shield.—

2. For who is God, but the Lord? And who is a rock ex-cept our God?— The God who gird-ed me with strength, and made my way so ver-y safe.—

3. He made my feet like hinds' feet— and set me se-cure up-on the heights.— He trains my hands for war, so my arms can bend a bow of— bronze.

4. Thou hast giv-en me the shield of Thy sal - va-tion, and Thy right hand held me high, and Thy help made me great. Thou didst give a wide place for my feet and they did not— slip.—

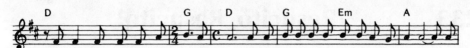

5. The Lord lives, and bless-ed be my rock, and ex-alt-ed be the God of my sal-va-tion.__ For

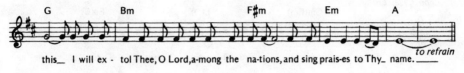

this__ I will ex-tol Thee, O Lord, a-mong the na-tions, and sing prais-es to Thy__ name. ____

to refrain

Yea, Thou dost light my lamp. ____

Psalm 150

232

Psalm 150 adapted by
Jan Vermulst

Music by
Jan Vermulst

REFRAIN
Capo 5, Play G

Al-le-lu-ia, al-le-lu-ia, al-le-lu-ja!

VERSES

1. Praise God in His ho-ly dwell-ing. __
2. Praise Him with the blast of trum-pet. __
3. Praise Him with re-sound-ing cym-bals, with
4. Praise God the al-might-y Fa-ther. __

Praise Him on His might-y throne. Praise Him for His won-der-ful
Praise Him now with lyre and harp. Praise Him with the tim-brel and
cym-bals that __ crash give praise. O, let ev-'ry-thing that has
Praise Christ, His be-lov-ed Son. Give praise to the Spir-it of

deeds. Praise Him for His sov'-reign maj-es-ty! ____
dance. Praise Him with the sound of string and reed! ____
breath, let all liv-ing crea-tures praise the Lord! ____
love. For-ev-ver the tri-une God be praised! ____

233 ¡Resucitó, Resucitó!

Words and Music by
Kiko Argüello

HE IS RISEN! ALLELUIA!
1. Death, where is death? Where is my death? Where is its victory?
2. Rejoice, brothers, for if today we love each other, it is because He is risen.
3. If we die with Him, we live with Him. We sing with Him, Alleluia!

Sing With All the Sons of Glory   234

Words by William J. Irons

Music by Ludwig van Beethoven
Arr. by Edward Hodges

235 Song of My People

Words and Music by
Juliet Pressel

A-bra-ham, A-bra-ham, where are you com-ing from, A-bra-ham?__ I'm
com-ing from the land of the pa-gans, Lord.__ I'm com-ing to You,__ my__ God.
A-bra-ham, A-bra-ham,____ I will be your God.
Is-ra-el, Is-ra-el, why have you strayed from me, Is-ra-el?__ You
say you don't need my__ guid-ing hand.__ You say you don't want my__ love.
Is-ra-el, Is-ra-el,____ I will be your God.
Gath-er 'round, lis-ten now to the words of a car-pen-ter__ Who
walked the earth__ work-ing mir-a-cles,__ Who died for us__ on a cross.

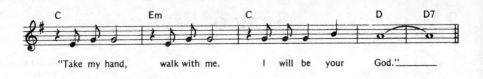

"Take my hand, walk with me. I will be your God."_____

Sons of men, sons of men, where are you com-ing from, sons of men?___ We're

com-ing to You__ out of dark-ness, Lord.___ We're com-ing to You,___ our___ God

Sons of men, sons of light,_____ I will be your God.

236   Song of Praise

Words and Music by
James Berlucchi

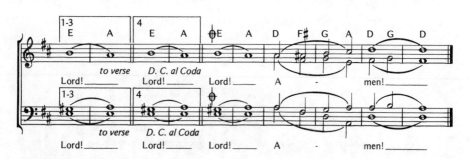

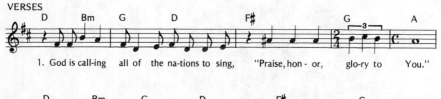

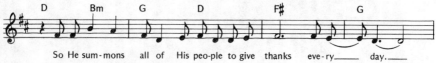

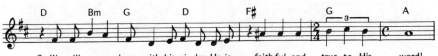

Thou-sands of voi-ces pro - claim, "God is light and He has_shone on us."_____

to refrain

2. We will see a horse with his ri-der, He is faith-ful and true to His word!

Crowned with glo-ry, eyes flam-ing fire,_ from His mouth is-sues a sword,_____ the

might-y word of God. King of kings and Lord of_ lords is He!_____

to refrain

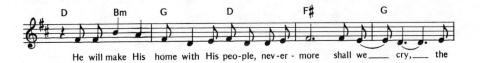

3. We a-wait our heav-en-ly cit-y sing-ing, "Je-ru-sa - lem, God has named you."

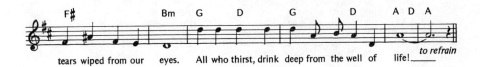

He will make His home with His peo-ple, nev-er - more shall we_____ cry,_____ the

tears wiped from our eyes. All who thirst, drink deep from the well of life!_____

to refrain

237 Song of Thanks

Words and Music by
Paul Quinlan

REFRAIN

Al - le - lu - ia, al - le - lu - ia, al - le - lu - ia, al - le - lu - ia, al - le - lu - ia, al - le - lu - ia, al - le - lu - ia, al - le - lu - ia. Al - le - lu - ia, al - le - lu - ia, al - le - lu - ia, al - le - lu - ia, al-

last time to Coda

- le - lu - ia, al - le - lu - ia, al - le - lu - ia, al - le - lu - ia. _____ *to verse*

- le - lu - ia, al - le - lu - ia, al - le - lu - ia, al - le - lu - ia! _____

VERSES

1. Sing a mer - ry song of thanks un - to the Lord.
2. In my troub - les all I go un - to the Lord.
3. All sur - round - ed when I strug - gled with my foe.
4. Loud re - joic - ing let there be in eve - ry home.
5. O - pen up _____ your gates of glo - ry; let me through.
6. Blest are they _____ who come _____ in the name of God.

1. Through-out eve - ry age His mer - cy will en - dure. Is - ra - el _____ will shout,
2. God is stand - ing by me; what man will I fear? To the Lord _____ we ran,
3. Aw - ful rag - ing fire; they buzz like an - gry bees. God then heard _____ my call,
4. God has come _____ to help us, strong and ver - y brave. Now I will _____ not die;
5. I'll give thanks _____ to God who saved my lone - ly life. This day God _____ has made;
6. God is Lord _____ of all; His light on us has shone. Let us play _____ a horn,

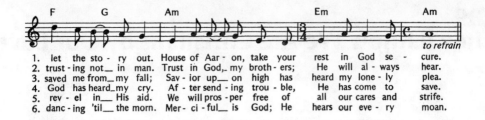

	F	G	Am		Em	Am

1. let the sto - ry out. House of Aar - on, take your rest in God se - cure.
2. trust - ing not in man. Trust in God, my broth - ers; He will al - ways hear.
3. saved me from my fall; Sav - ior up - on high has heard my lone - ly plea.
4. God has heard my cry. Af - ter send - ing trou - ble, He has come to save.
5. rev - el in His aid. We will pros - per free of all our cares and strife.
6. danc - ing 'til the morn. Mer - ci - ful is God; He hears our eve - ry moan.

to refrain

Therefore the Redeemed 238

Isaiah 51:11

Words and Music by
Ruth Lake

Capo 1, Play A

There-fore the re-deemed of the Lord shall re-turn and come with sing-ing un-to Zi - on, and ev - er - last - ing joy shall be up - on their head. There-fore the re-head. They shall ob - tain glad - ness and joy, and sor - row and mourn - ing shall flee a way.

There-fore the re-deemed of the Lord shall re-turn and come with sing-ing un-to Zi - on, and ev - er - last - ing joy shall be up - on their head.

239
They'll Know We Are Christians by Our Love

Words and Music by
Peter Scholtes

VERSES

1. We are one in the Spir - it, We are one in the Lord, We are
2. We will walk with each oth - er, We will walk hand in hand, We will
3. We will work with each oth - er, We will work side by side, We will
4. All praise to the Fa - ther, From whom all things come, And all

one in the Spir - it, We are one in the Lord, And we
walk with each oth - er, We will walk hand in hand, And to-
work with each oth - er, We will work side by side, And we'll
praise to Christ Je - sus, His on - ly Son, And all

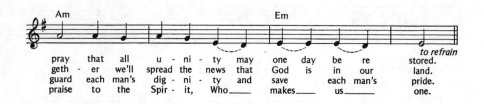

to refrain

pray that all u - ni - ty may one day be re stored.
geth - er we'll spread the news that God is in our land.
guard each man's dig - ni - ty and save each man's pride.
praise to the Spir - it, Who makes us one.

REFRAIN

And they'll know we are Christ-ians by our love, by our love, Yes they'll

know we are Christ - ians by our love.

Thou Art Worthy

240

Revelation 4:11

Words and Music by
Pauline M. Mills

Thou art wor-thy. Thou art wor-thy. Thou art wor-thy, O Lord.___

Thou art wor-thy to re-ceive glo-ry, glo-ry and hon-or and power.___ For

Thou hast cre-a-ted, hast all things cre-a-ted, for Thou hast cre-a-ted all things.___

And for Thy pleas-ure they are cre-a-ted. Thou art wor-thy, O Lord.___

Worthy Is the Lord

241

Words and Music by
Mark S. Kinzer

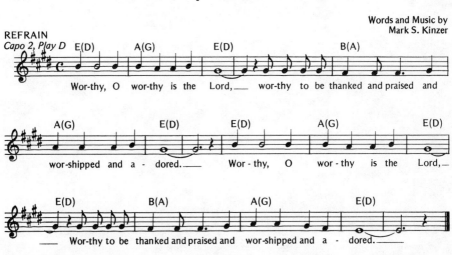

Wor-thy, O wor-thy is the Lord,___ wor-thy to be thanked and praised and

wor-shipped and a-dored.___ Wor-thy, O wor-thy is the Lord,___

___ Wor-thy to be thanked and praised and wor-shipped and a-dored.___

All Hail the Power of Jesus' Name 301

Words by
Edward Perronet
Alt. by John Rippon

'Coronation'

Music by
Oliver Holden

1. All hail the pow'r of Je - sus' name! Let an - gels pros - trate fall; Bring
2. Ye cho - sen seed of Is - rael's race, Ye ran-somed from the fall, Hail
3. Let ev - 'ry kin - dred, ev - 'ry tribe, On this ter - res - trial ball, To
4. O that with yon - der sa - cred throng We at His feet may fall! We'll

forth the roy - al di - a - dem, And crown Him Lord of___ all; Bring
Him who saves you by___ His - grace, And crown Him Lord of___ all; Hail
Him all maj - es - ty___ as - cribe, And crown Him Lord of___ all; To
join the ev - er - last - ing___song, And crown Him Lord of___ all; We'll

forth the roy - al di - a - dem, And crown Him Lord___ of all!
Him who saves you by___His___grace, And crown Him Lord___ of all!
Him all maj - es - ty___ as - cribe, And crown Him Lord___ of all!
join the ev - er - last - ing___ song, And crown Him Lord___ of all!

302
All I Want

Phil. 3:8-10 adapted by
John Bagniewski

Music by
John Bagniewski

1. I be- lieve that noth- ing can out- weigh the ad- van- tage of know- ing Je- sus Christ, the ad- van- tage of know- ing Christ Je- sus my Lord.

REFRAIN
All I want is to know Je- sus Christ and the pow- er of His ris- ing. All I want is to know my Lord and in Him to a- bide... Ooh... Ooh...

VERSES
2. For Him I take the loss of eve- ry- thing, and I look on eve- ry thing as naught, if on- ly I have Christ and a place in Him. *to refrain*

3. I'm no long- er try- ing on my own for per- fec- tion com- ing from the law; I want on- ly that which comes through my faith in Him. *to refrain*

Awake, O Israel

303

Several Old Testament passages
Adapted by Merla Watson

Music by
Merla Watson

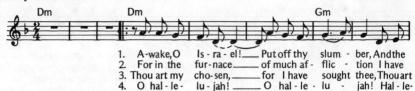

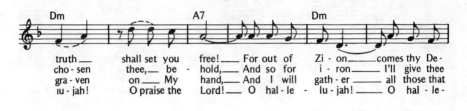

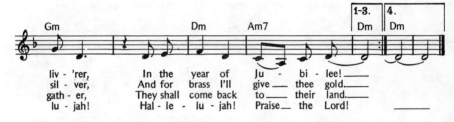

1. A-wake, O Is - ra - el! Put off thy slum - ber, And the
2. For in the fur-nace of much af - flic - tion I have
3. Thou art my cho-sen, for I have sought thee, Thou art
4. O hal - le - lu - jah! O hal - le - lu - jah! Hal - le -

truth shall set you free! For out of Zi - on comes thy De -
cho - sen thee, be - hold, And so for i - ron I'll give thee
gra - ven on My hand, And I will gath - er all those that
lu - jah! O praise the Lord! O hal - le - lu - jah! O hal - le -

liv - 'rer, In the year of Ju - bi - lee!
sil - ver, And for brass I'll give thee gold.
gath - er, They shall come back to their land.
lu - jah! Hal - le - lu - jah! Praise the Lord!

304 Battle Hymn of the Republic

Words by
Julia W. Howe *Capo 1, Play A*

Music by
William Steffe

VERSES Bb (A)

1. Mine eyes have seen the glo-ry of the com-ing of the Lord; He is
2. I have seen Him in the watch-fires of a hun-dred cir-cling camps; They have
3. He has sound-ed forth the trum-pet that shall nev-er sound re-treat; He is
4. In the beau-ty of the lil-ies, Christ was born a-cross the sea, With a

Eb (D)   Bb (A)

tram-pling out the vin-tage where the grapes of wrath are stored; He hath
build-ed Him an al-tar in the eve-ning dews and damps; I can
sift-ing out the hearts of men be-fore His judg-ment seat; O be
glo-ry in His bos-om that trans-fig-ures you and me; As He

Bb (A)   Cm (Bm) F (E) Bb (A)

loosed the fate-ful light-ning of His ter-ri-ble swift sword; His truth is march-ing on.
read His right-eous sen-tence by the dim and flar-ing lamps; His day is march-ing on.
swift, my soul, to an-swer Him! be ju-bi-lant, my feet! Our God is march-ing on.
died to make men ho-ly, let us live to make men free, While God is march-ing on.

REFRAIN
Bb (A)   Eb (D)   Bb (A)

Glo-ry! glo-ry, hal-le-lu-jah! Glo-ry! glo-ry, hal-le-lu-jah!
Glo-ry! glo-ry, hal-le-lu-jah! Glo-ry! glo-ry, hal-le-lu-jah!
Glo-ry! glo-ry, hal-le-lu-jah! Glo-ry! glo-ry, hal-le-lu-jah!
Glo-ry! glo-ry, hal-le-lu-jah! Glo-ry! glo-ry, hal-le-lu-jah!

Bb (A)   Cm (Bm) F (E) Bb (A)

Glo-ry! glo-ry, hal-le-lu-jah! His truth is march-ing on.
Glo-ry! glo-ry, hal-le-lu-jah! His day is march-ing on.
Glo-ry! glo-ry, hal-le-lu-jah! Our God is march-ing on.
Glo-ry! glo-ry, hal-le-lu-jah! While God is march-ing on.

Be Exalted, O God

305

Psalm 57:9-11

Capo 3, Play G

Music by
Brent Chambers

I will give thanks to Thee, O Lord, a-mong the peo-ple. I will sing prais-es to Thee a-mong the na-tions. For Thy stead-fast love is great, is great to the heav-ens, and Thy faith-ful-ness, Thy faith-ful-ness to the clouds. Be ex-alt-ed, O God, a-bove the heav-ens. Let Thy glo-ry be o-ver all the earth. Be ex-glo-ry be o-ver all the earth. I will glo - ry, let Thy glo - ry, let Thy glo-ry be o-ver all the earth.

306 Behold

Based on Isaiah 12:2

Music by
Stuart Dauermann

Be-hold,___ God is my Sal-

va-tion;___ I will trust and will not be a-fraid.___

___ For the Lord my God is my Strength and my Song; He

al-so has be-come my Sal-va-tion.___ For the Lord my

God is my Strength and my Song; He al-so has be-come my Sal-

va-tion.___ La la la la la la la la la la la la la la la la

la la la la la la la la la la la la la la la la la la la

la la la la la la la la la la la la la la la la.___ La la la

la.___ Be-la la la la la la la la.

Blessing and Glory

307

Revelation 7:12, 11:15, and 12:10

Capo 1, Play D

REFRAIN *(Sing twice at the beginning and the end.)*

Music by
John Keating

308 Come and Worship

Words and Music by
A. Carter

Come and wor - ship, ___ roy - al priest - hood. ___

___ Come and praise Him, ___ Ho - ly Na - tion. ___ Wor - ship

Je - sus, ___ our Re - deem - er. ___ He is pre - cious, ___

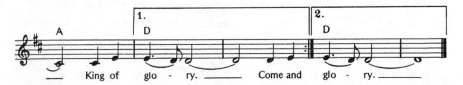

1. ___ King of glo - ry. ___ Come and **2.** glo - ry. ___

Come Back Singing

309

Psalm 126 adapted by
John Bagniewski

Music by
John Bagniewski

Capo 5, Play C

1. When Yah - weh brought the cap - tives home to Zi - on,___ it seemed like a dream to us at first.___ Then our mouths were filled with laugh - ter, laugh - ter, and on our lips a song.___ Come back sing - ing car - ry - ing the wheat,___ Hav - ing gone in weep - ing with the seeds.___ Now re - turn the har - vest with a song.___ Come back sing - ing car - ry - ing the wheat.___ Come back sing - ing car - ry - ing the wheat.___

2. The pa - gans, e - ven they, be - gan to tell___ the mar - vels the Lord had done for us.___ And, in deed, He did for us great mar - vels. How o - ver - joyed we were.

3. Oh Yah - weh, bring all cap - tives back a - gain,___ like tor - rents up - on an ar - id land.___ Those who went to sow in tears and weep - ing will sing now as they reap.

1-2. 2. The 3. Oh

3. *ritard*

310 Come, Holy Spirit

Words and Music by
Mary Ackroyd

Crown Him With Many Crowns 311

'Diademata'

Words by
Matthew Bridges

Music by
George J. Elvey

1. Crown Him with man - y crowns, the Lamb up - on His throne; Hark!
2. Crown Him the Lord of life, Who tri - umphed o'er the grave, Who
3. Crown Him the Lord of Lords, Who o - ver all doth reign, Who
4. Crown Him the Lord of heav'n, one with the Fa - ther known, One

how the heav'n - ly an - them drowns all mu - sic but its own. A -
rose vic - to - rious in the strife for those He came to save. His
once on earth, the in - car - nate Word, for ran - somed sin - ners slain, Now
with the Spir - it giv'n through Him from yon - der glo - rious throne. To

wake, my soul, and sing of Him Who died for thee, And
glo - ries now we sing, Who died and rose on high, Who
lives in realms of light, where saints with an - gels sing Their
Thee be end - less praise, for Thou for us hast died. Be

hail Him as thy match - less King through all e - ter - ni - ty.
died e - ter - nal life to bring and lives that death may die.
songs be - fore Him day and night, their God, Re - deem - er, King.
Thou, O Lord, through end - less days a - dored and mag - ni - fied.

312 For God So Loved

Based on John 3:16-17, John 1:12

Music by
Stuart Dauermann

For God so loved the world that He gave— His on - ly be - got - ten

Son, That who - so - ev - er be - lieves in — Him— should not per -

ish, but have life ev - er - last - ing, have life ev - er - last - ing,

have life ev - er - last - ing, have life ev - er - last - ing. For

God so loved the world that He gave— His on - ly be - got - ten

Son. For God did not send His Son in - to the world

to bring con - dem - na - tion, But rath - er that, through the re -

ceiv - ing of Him, men might find true sal - va - tion, and *D.S al Coda*

He came in - to the world and He dwelt a - mong His own; But His

313   Glorious in Majesty

'Shibbolet Basadeh'

Words by
Jeff Cothran

Traditional Jewish Melody
Arr. by Jeff Cothran

Guitar, Piano, or Recorder
Introduction and Optional Interlude

(Triangle)

VERSES

Guitar chords are for rehearsal only

1. Glo - ri - ous in ma - jes - ty, ho - ly in His prais - es,
2. Vic - to - ry He won for us, free - ing us from dark - ness,
3. Breth - er - en, we live in love, liv - ing with each oth - er,

(doo)

Je - sus, our Sa - vior and our King. Born a man yet God of old,
dy - ing and ris - ing from the dead. Liv - ing with the Fa - ther now,
glad - ly we share each oth - er's pain. Yet He will not leave us so,

let us all a - dore Him; filled with His Spir - it, let us sing.
yet He is a - mong us; we are the bo - dy, He the head.
soon He is re - turn - ing, tak - ing us back with Him to reign.

REFRAIN

Liv - ing is to love Him, serv - ing Him to know His free - dom.

Come a - long with us to join the praise of Je - sus.

(Observe repeat sign after Verse 3.)

(last time)

Come to Je - sus now. Go to live His Word re - joic - ing.
(doo)

314

Glory Be to Jesus

Viva! Viva! Gesu (18th c. Italian hymn)
Translated by Edward Caswall, 1857.

Music by
Friedrich Filitz

Capo 5, Play C

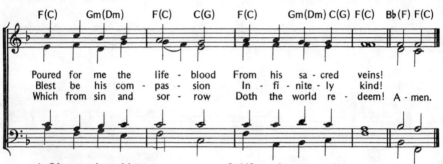

1. Glo - ry be to Je - sus, Who in bit - ter pains
2. Grace and life e - ter - nal In that blood I find,
3. Blest through end - less a - ges Be the pre - cious stream

Poured for me the life - blood From his sa - cred veins!
Blest be his com - pas - sion In - fi - nite - ly kind!
Which from sin and sor - row Doth the world re - deem! A - men.

4. Oft as earth exulting
   Wafts its praise on high,
   Angel hosts, rejoicing,
   Make their glad reply.

5. Lift ye then your voices;
   Swell the mighty flood;
   Louder still and louder
   Praise the precious blood.   Amen.

God Is Raising an Army 315

Words and Music by
Mark Cowen

Capo 3, Play D

REFRAIN *(Sing twice at the end.)*

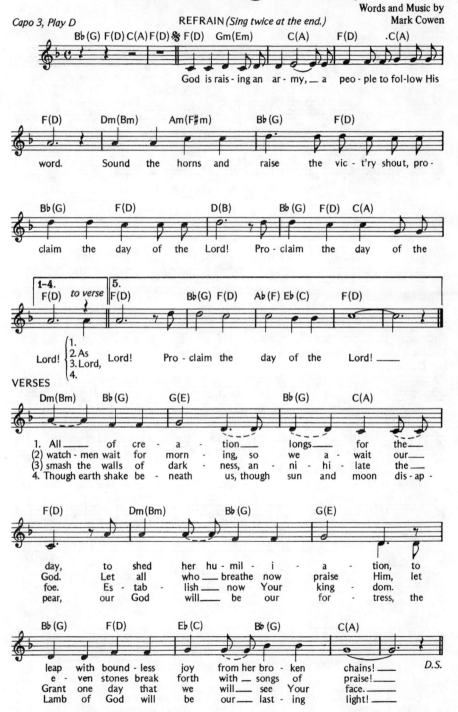

God is rais-ing an ar-my, __ a peo-ple to fol-low His word. Sound the horns and raise the vic-t'ry shout, pro-claim the day of the Lord! Pro-claim the day of the

1-4. Lord! *to verse*
5. Lord! Pro-claim the day of the Lord! ___

VERSES

1. All ___ of cre - a - tion ___ longs ___ for the ___ day, to shed her hu-mil - i - a - tion, to leap with bound-less joy from her bro-ken chains! ___
(2) watch-men wait for morn - ing, so we a-wait our ___ God. Let all who ___ breathe now praise Him, let e - ven stones break forth with ___ songs of praise! ___
(3) smash the walls of dark - ness, an - ni - hi - late the ___ foe. Es - tab - lish ___ now Your king - dom. Grant one day that we will ___ see Your face. ___
4. Though earth shake be - neath us, though sun and moon dis-ap - pear, our God will ___ be our for - tress, the Lamb of God will be our ___ last - ing light! ___

D.S.

316 God, Make Us Your Family

Adapted from
Isaiah 35

Words and Music by
Tim Whipple

Capo 3, Play Dm

1. The eyes of the blind shall be o-pened, the ears of the deaf shall hear. The chains of the lame will be bro-ken, streams will flow in des-erts of fear. Your

REFRAIN

king - dom come, your will be done, now that we have be-come your sons. Let the prayer of our hearts dai - ly be: God, make us your fam - i - ly. God, make us your fam - i - ly.

2. The
3. The

VERSES 2 & 3

(2.) ran-somed of the Lord shall re - turn, the is-lands will sing his songs at last.
(3.) na - tions will see their shame, the one true God will be a-dored.

The chaff from the wheat shall be burned, his king-dom on earth, it shall
They turn from their for - tune and shame, his ho - ly moun-tain shall

1.
come to pass. Your

2.
stored. Your

be re God, make us your fam - i - ly.

Optional refrains:

Laude, Lauda, Laude, Lauda. } repeat
Gloria, Emmanuel.

Alleluia, Alleluia } repeat
Glory to the living God.

Great and Wonderful

317

Based on Revelation 15:4

Music by
Stuart Dauermann

Great and won-der-ful are Thy won-drous deeds,_

O Lord God, the Al - might - ty. _ Just and true are_ all Thy

ways, O Lord;_ King of the a - ges art Thou._ Who shall not fear and

glo - ri - fy Thy_ name, O Lord? For Thou a - lone art ho - ly

Thou _ a - lone._ All the na - tions shall come and

wor - ship Thee,_ For Thy glo - ry shall be re - veal - ed. Hal - le-

lu - jah!_ Hal - le - lu - jah!_ Hal - le - lu - jah! A - men._ La la la

la la._ la la la la la la_ la la la la la la_

la la la la la la_ la la la_ la la la la la la_ la la

1,3. la la la la la la._ **2.** La la la la. **4.** la.

318 Hail to the Lord's Anointed

Based on Psalm 72
James Montgomery 1771-1854

'Yeldall'

Music by
Betty Pulkingham

1. Hail to the Lord's a-noint-ed, Great Da-vid's great-er Son!__ Hail in the time ap-point-ed, His reign on earth be-gun! He comes to break op-pres-sion, To set the cap - tive free;____ To take a - way trans-gres - sion, And rule in e - qui - ty.

2. He shall come down like show-ers Up - on the fruit - ful earth,__ And love, joy, hope, like flow - ers, Spring in his path to birth: _____ Be-fore him on the moun-tains Shall peace, the her - ald, go;_____ And right-eous - ness in foun - tains From hill to val - ley__ flow.

3. Kings shall bow down be-fore_him, And gold and in - cense bring;__ All na - tions shall a-dore__him, His praise all peo - ple sing;_____ For he shall have do - min - ion O'er eve - ry sea__ and__ shore;_____ His king-dom still in - creas - ing, A king - dom__ for ev - er__ more.

4. O'er eve - ry foe vic-tor-i - ous, He on his throne shall rest;____ From age to age more glo - ri -ous, All bless-ing and all - blest:_____ The tide of time shall nev - er His cov - e - nant__ re - move;_____ His name shall stand for - ev - er, His change - less name__ of __ love.

1-3. D Am7
4. D Am7 D
D.S.

Hevenu Shalom Aleikhem 319

Traditional

He - ve - nu sha - lom a - leik - hem, he - ve - nu

sha - lom a - leik - hem, he - ve - nu sha - lom a - leik - hem, he - ve - nu

sha - lom, sha - lom, sha - lom, a - leik - hem. He - ve - nu sha - lom a - leik - hem! Hey!

We bring you peace.

Hiney Mah Tov 320

Psalm 133:1

Traditional

Hin - ey mah tov u
hold, how good and—

mah na - im, shev - et a - chim gam yach - ad. Hin -
pleas - ant it is for breth - ren to dwell to - geth - er. Be -

ey mah tov u - mah na - im, shev - et a - chim gam
Hold, how good and— pleas - ant it is for breth - ren to dwell to -

yach - ad. Hin - ey mah tov, hin - ey mah tov. La la
geth - er. In u - ni - ty, to dwell in u - ni - ty. La la

la, la la la la la la la. Hin - ey mah tov, hin - ey mah
la, la la la la la la la. In u - ni - ty, to dwell in u - ni

tov. La la la, la la la la la la la. Be -
ty. La la la, la la la la la la la.

321 I Will Sing, I Will Sing

Words and Music by
Max Dyer

I will sing, I will sing a song___ un-to the Lord. I will
lu, al-le-lu-ia, glo___ ry to the Lord. Al-le-

sing, I will sing a song___ un-to the Lord. I will sing, I will sing a song___
lu, al-le-lu-ia, glo___ ry to the Lord. Al-le- lu, al-le-lu-ia, glo___

___ un-to the Lord. Al-le- lu___ ia, glo- ry to the Lord. Al-le-
___ ry to the Lord. Al-le- lu- ia, glo- ry to the Lord.

Optional verses:

We will come, we will come as one before the Lord.
   Alleluia, glory to the Lord.
If the Son, if the Son shall make you free,
   you shall be free indeed.
They that sow in tears shall reap in joy.
   Alleluia, glory to the Lord.
Ev'ry knee shall bow and ev'ry tongue confess
   that Jesus Christ is Lord.
In his name, in his name we have the victory.
   Alleluia, glory to the Lord.

322 Isaiah 43

Isaiah 43
Adapted by Cathy Zawacki

Music by
Cathy Zawacki

REFRAIN A

Yah-weh, You have__ cre - a-ted me.__ You have called me by name,___

and I __ am __ Yours. to Refrain B Yours. to verse 2, 3, 4

REFRAIN B

For-ev-er__ I will sing of Your good-ness. __ I will walk now in free - dom__

323 Let us Come and Bow Down

Words and Music by
James Berlucchi

REFRAIN

Let us come and bow down be - fore_ our God and King:_ "My glo - ry and the lift - er of_ my head."_ Let us come and sac - ri - fice eve - ry - thing_ to the One who raised_Christ Je - sus from the dead. _

1,4. | 2,3. _to verse_ | 5.

Let us _

VERSES

1. Let us not_ lose heart in run - ning the race._

Let us look to Je - sus the found - er of our faith.

Let us lift_ our droop - ing hands and strength - en our knees_

to fol - low the Lord, our God, the King of Kings._ Let us

2. For who is like _____ the Lord, _____ our sav - ior? _____

Search the heav - ens, search the earth; there is none _____ like Him. _____

Ho - ly, Ho - ly Lord God Al - might - y, _____

all cre - a - tion is full of Your glo - ry. _____ Let us

Verses may be improvised, using the two above as models.

324 Let Us Give Thanks

Adapted from
Luke 10: 17, John 10: 10

Words and Music by
Brian Howard

G   C   G   C

REFRAIN

Let_____ us give thanks_____ that our_ names are writ-ten,

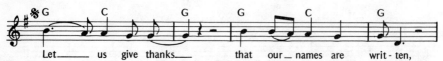

Let_____ us give thanks_____ that our_ names are writ-ten,

Writ-ten in the book of life_____ and in-scribed up-on_ His palms,

Writ-ten in the book of life_____ and in-scribed up-on_ His palms.

VERSES

1. Re-joice not_____ that dev-ils_____ flee in His name._

Re-joice not_____ in the pow-er that He gave._

For He came_____ to break the_____ bonds of sin._

325   Let Us Sing

Words and Music by
Roger L. Holtz

REFRAIN *(Sing twice at the beginning and the end.)*

Let us sing to the Lord with our whole heart. Let us sing to the Lord with our whole strength. Let us of-fer the Lord a sac-ri-fice of praise, for He has done mar-vel-ous things. *to verse* things.

VERSES

1. We will no lon-ger be a-fraid. We will wear the whole ar-mor of our God. We will march on to war be-neath the ban-ner of the Lord and be vic-to-ri-ous ev-er-more. Let us

It is customary to improvise verses for this song, using the chord progression of the printed verse.

Lion of Judah

326

Words and Music by
Ted Sandquist

1., 4. Li - on of Ju - dah, on the throne, __
2. Li - on of Ju - dah, come to earth, __
3. Li - on of Ju - dah, come a - gain, __

I shout Your name. __ Let it be known that You are
I want to thank __ You for Your birth. For the
Take up Your throne, __ Je - ru - sa - lem. Bring re -

King of Kings, __ You are __ the Prince __ of Peace. May Your
liv - ing Word, __ For Your __ death on __ the tree, For Your
lease to this earth, and the con - sum - ma - tion of Your

King - dom's reign __ nev - er cease! Hail to __ the King! __ Hail to __ the
res - ur - rec - tion vic - to - ry! Hal - le - lu - jah! __ Hal - le - lu -
king - dom's reign, __ let __ it come! Mar - a - na - tha! __ Mar - a - na -

1-3. **4.**

King! __ __ Hail to __ the King! __ Hail to __ the
jah! __
tha! __

King! You are my King! Hail to __ the King!

327 The Lord Is Blessing Me Right Now

Capo 1, Play G

Unknown

Ab(G) ... **Ab(G)** ... **Eb(D)**

The Lord is bless-ing me___ right now, right now. The

Eb7(D7) ... **Ab(G)**

Lord is bless-ing me___ right now, right now. You may not be

Ab7(G7) ... **Bbm(Am)** ... **Ab(G)**

a-ble to see___ all the Lord has done for me,___ but the Lord___ is

1. repeat ad libitum
Ab(G) ... **Db(C) Ab(G) Eb(D) Ab(G)** ... **2. last time only Ab(G)**

bless-ing me___ right now, right now. The bless-ing me,___ but the Lord___ is

Ab(G) ... **Db(C) Ab(G) Eb(D) Ab(G)**

bless-ing me,___ but the Lord___ is bless-ing me ___right now, right now.

Copyright unknown.

328

Luke 1:46-55

Adapted by Charles Christmas

The Magnificat

REFRAIN

Music by
Charles Christmas

Am G C ... **C** ... **G**

My soul___ mag-ni-fies the

My soul mag-ni-fies the

C ... **Dm** ... **Em**

Lord,___ and my spir-it___ re-joic-es___ in

Lord. My spir-it re-joic-es in

F G ... **1-3. C** ... *to verse* ... **4. C** ... *to Coda*

God___ my Sav-ior.___ Sav-ior.___ My

God___ my Sav-ior.___ Sav-ior.___

{ 1. For
{ 2. He
{ 3. The

Copyright © 1978 The Word of God, P.O. Box 8617, Ann Arbor, MI 48107 U.S.A. All rights reserved. BMI

VERSES

329 My Glory and the Lifter of My Head

Adapted from
Psalm 3:3-4

Words and Music by
Mae McAlister

My glo-ry and the lift-er of my head, my glo-ry and the lift-er of my head! And Thou, O Lord, art a shield to me,— my glo-ry and the lift-er of my head! I cried un-to the Lord with my voice!— cried un-to the Lord with my voice! I cried un-to the Lord with my voice,— and He heard me out of His ho-ly hill!— My glo-ry and the lift-er of my head, my glo-ry and the lift-er of my head!— And Thou, O Lord, art a shield to me,— my glo-ry and the lift-er of my head! My head!

Now Let Us Sing
'Let Us Sing Till the Power of the Lord Come Down'

330

Words and Music by
A.B. Windom

331 Once No People

Based on I Peter 2:9-10
Maggie Durran

Music by
Betty Pulkingham

REFRAIN

For we are a cho-sen race, a roy-al priest-hood, ho-ly na-tion. Once no peo-ple, now God's peo-ple, pro-claim - ing His mar - vel-ous light. *to verse*

VERSES

1. Sing the songs of faith - ful Zi - on, we are the stars and the grains of sand. Through our faith we are made glo - ri-ous, we are sons of A - bra - ham.
2. Dance the steps of joy - ful Zi - on, cym-bals, harps, and tam - bour - ines. Blow the trum - pet, sound the glo - ry, in the pres - ence of the Lord.
3. Taste the fruit of peace - ful val - leys, sip of the wine and eat the bread. Know the shep - herd who is guid - ing, the Lord, the Lamb of God.

D.S.

4. We will serve through trib - u - la - tion, we will fol - low to the cross. Know the death and pain of suf - fer - ing, God wipes the tears from our eyes.

D.S. al Coda

Now God's peo - ple, pro - claim - ing His mar - vel - ous light. _____

light, _____ pro - claim - ing His mar - vel - ous light. _____

332 Proclaim His Marvelous Deeds

Psalm 96 adapted by
Donald E. Fishel

Music by
Donald E. Fishel

4. Wor - ship the LORD __ in ho - ly at - tire. __ Trem - ble be - fore __ him,

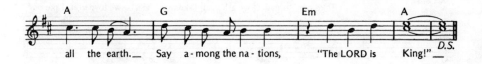

all the earth. __ Say a - mong the na - tions, "The LORD is King!" __

D.S.

St. Patrick's Breastplate   333

Words attributed to
St. Patrick

'Bunessan'

Gaelic Melody

1. Christ be be - side me, Christ be be -
2. Christ on my right hand, Christ on my
3. Christ be in all hearts think - ing a -

fore ____ me, Christ be be - hind me, King of my heart. __
left ____ hand, Christ all a - round me, shield in the strife __
bout ____ me; Christ be on all tongues tell - ing of me. __

Christ be with - in me, Christ be be - low me, Christ be a -
Christ in my sleep - ing, Christ in my sit - ting, Christ in my
Christ be the vis - ion in eyes that see me; in ears that

1,2.   3.

bove me, nev - er to part. __
ris - ing, light of my life.
hear me, Christ ev - er be. __

334 Take Our Bread

Words and music by
Joseph Wise

REFRAIN

Take our bread, we ask you; take our hearts, we love you. Take our
lives, oh Fa-ther; we are yours, we are yours. yours.

VERSES

1. Yours as we stand at the ta-ble you set; Yours as we
eat the bread our hearts can't for-get. We are the sign of your
life with us yet, we are yours, we are yours. Take our *D.S.*

2. Your ho-ly peo-ple stand-ing washed in your blood, Spir-it-filled yet
hun-gry we a-wait your food. We are poor, but we've brought our-selves
the best we could; we are yours, we are yours. Take our *D.S.*

335 Trees of the Field

Isaiah 55:12 adapted by
Steffi Geiser-Rubin

Music by
Stuart Dauermann

You shall go out with joy___ and be led
forth with peace.___ The moun-tains and the hills will break forth be-

336 Unto the House of the Lord

Psalm 122 adapted by
John Bagniewski
Capo 3, Play D

Music by
John Bagniewski

REFRAIN

I re-joiced when they said to me, "Let us go___ un-to the house of the Lord," stand-ing there, O Je-ru-sa-lem,___ in your gates___ un-to the house of the Lord. ___

VERSES

1. Look up-on Je-ru - sa-lem,___ the cit - y now re-stored.___
2. As He or-dered Is - ra - el,___ they come to praise His name___
3. Pray for peace, Je-ru - sa-lem,___ pros-per - i - ty at home,___
4. Since we are God's peo - ple, ___ I say, "Peace be to you!" ___

Here the tribes of Yah - weh come___ as one un - to the Lord.___
Here where courts of jus - tice,___ the courts of Da - vid, reign.___
Peace in - side your cit - y walls___ that comes from God a - lone.___
May the God who dwells___ in us___ your hap - pi - ness re - new.___

337 We Will Sing to the Lord Our God

Words and Music by
Richard Gullen

We will sing to the Lord___ our God, ___ might - y and splen - did is He!___

338

You Are Near

Psalm 139 adapted by
Dan Schutte, S.J.

Music by
Dan Schutte S.J.

Chords: C9, Am7/G, C/B, D/F#

REFRAIN

G   C9   G   D   C9
Yah-weh, I know you are near,___ stand-ing al-ways

Am7 Am7/G G D C9 Bm
at my side.___ You guard me from the foe, and you

C C/B Am7 Am7/G | 1-4. G *to verse* | 5. G
lead me in ways ev-er-last-ing.___ last-ing.___

VERSES

G   C9   D   Em   Am
1. Lord, you have searched my heart, and you know when I sit and when I

Bm   Em   Am   Bm
stand. Your__ hand is up-on me pro-tect-ing me from death,

Am7 *slowing* Am7/G D/F# *ritard*
keep-ing me from harm.___   D.S.

G   C9   D   Em   Am
2. Where can I run from your love? If I climb to the heav-ens you are

Bm   Em   Am   Bm
there; if I fly to the sun-rise or sail be-yond the sea,

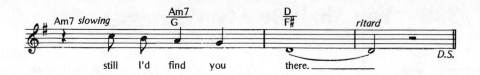

still I'd find you there._____

D.S.

3. You know my heart and its ways, you who formed me be-fore I was

born in the se - cret of dark - ness be - fore I saw the sun

in **my** moth - er's womb._____

D.S.

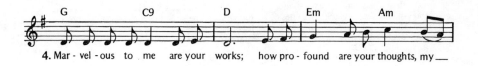

4. Mar - vel - ous to me are your works; how pro - found are your thoughts, my ___

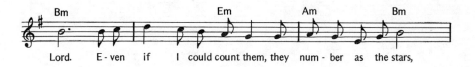

Lord. E - ven if I could count them, they num - ber as the stars,

you would still be there._____

D.S.

339 You Shall Be My Witnesses

Words and Music by
Sr. Mary Mc Cooey, H.R.S.

with spirit

You___ shall be my wit-ness-es

un - to the ends of the earth, wit-ness-ing to my

truth and to my love.___

1. If you fol-low___ in my foot-steps,___
2. If you a - bide___ in__ me,___
3. If you love___ one an-oth - er, ___
4. If you are filled___ with the Spir - it,___

you shall be my wit - ness, if you take___ up__ your __
you shall be my wit - ness, for with me in___ you, — you _
you shall be my wit - ness, for then eve - ry - one___ will _
you shall be my wit - ness. What to say will be giv-en you, so__

cross and fol-low me___ and__ do__ not__ be__ a -
will bear fruit in plen - ty, a___ fruit__ that__ will__ re -
know that you are mine, ___ when you love__ one an - oth - er in
do not be a - fraid, ___ for__ he who is the Spir - it__ of your

| 1-3. | | 4. | D.S. al Coda |

fraid,___ but be - lieve__ in___ me.
main,___ a___ fruit__ that will last.
truth, ___ as___ I have loved__ you.
Fa - ther__ will__   speak in you.

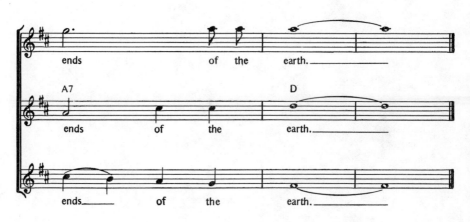

Ascribe to the Lord

401

Words adapted from Psalm 29 by
James Berlucchi

Music by
James Berlucchi

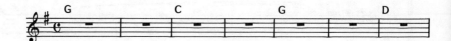

VERSE 1

WOMEN: 1. A - scribe to the Lord,____ O____ heav'n - ly beings,

a-scribe to him glo - ry___ and strength. O come a - scribe to the Lord

____ the glo-ry of his name, and wor-ship him___ in ho - ly___ ar - ray.

MEN: The voice of God is up - on man-y wa - ters.___ The God of glo - ry___

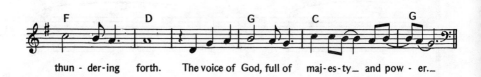

thun - der - ing forth. The voice of God, full of maj-es-ty___ and pow - er.___

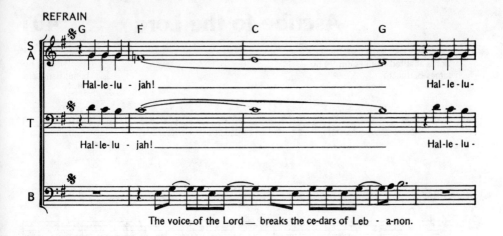

The voice of the Lord — breaks the ce-dars of Leb - a-non.

The voice of the Lord — flash-es forth flames of fire.— The voice of the Lord

—strips the oaks and for - ests bare. And in his tem-ple all _cry, "Glo-ry!"_

402 Be With Me, Lord

Psalm 91

Music by
Donald E. Fishel

REFRAIN

Be with me, Lord,___ when I am in trou - ble.___ Be with me, Lord.___ Be

1. Lord.___ Be

2-4. Lord.___ **5.** Lord.___ **6.** Lord.___

1.
2. No
3. Up -
4. Be-cause he

VERSES

1. You who dwell in the shel - ter, in the shel - ter of the Most_High, who a - bide_ in the shad-ow of the Al - might-y,___ Say to the LORD,___ "My ref - uge_ and my for - tress, my_ God, in whom I trust."___ Be e - vil shall be - fall _you, no_ e - vil shall be - fall _you, nor shall af -

403   Blessed Be the Lord, My Rock

Psalm 144 adapted by
Mark B. Foster

Music by
Mark B. Foster

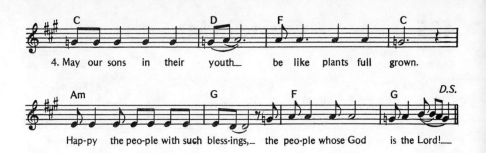

4. May our sons in their youth— be like plants full grown.

Hap-py the peo-ple with such bless-ings,— the peo-ple whose God is the Lord!—

The Celebration Song

404

Psalm 22:3,25
Adapted by Brent Chambers

Music by
Brent Chambers

In the pres-ence of Your peo-ple
Lai lai lai lai lai lai lai lai,

I will praise Your name, for a - lone You are ho - ly, en-
lai lai lai lai lai. Lai lai lai lai lai lai lai lai

throned on the prais-es of Is - ra - el. Let us cel - e-brate Your good-ness
lai lai lai lai lai lai lai lai lai. Lai lai lai lai lai lai lai lai,

and Your stead - fast love. May Your name be ex - alt - ed
lai lai lai lai lai. Lai lai lai lai lai lai lai

1. here on — earth and in heav'n a - bove.
2. lai lai— lai lai lai lai lai lai.

405

Create in Me

Psalm 51 adapted by
George Misulia

Music by
George Misulia

Capo 2, Play D

REFRAIN

Cre - ate in me a clean heart,—— put a new and right Spir - it with - in me. Cast me— not a - way from your pres - ence, and take not your Ho - ly Spir - it—— from me.

to verse

Cre - ate in me a clean heart.————

VERSES

1. Have mer-cy on me, O God,— in your good-ness. In your com - pas - sion, blot out all my sin. Thor-ough-ly cleanse me from

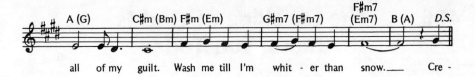

A (G)　　C#m (Bm) F#m (Em)　　G#m7 (F#m7)　F#m7 (Em7)　B (A)　D.S.

all　of my　guilt. Wash me till I'm　whit - er than　snow.___　Cre -

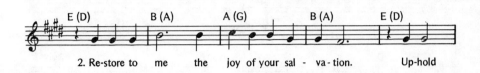

E (D)　　B (A)　　A (G)　　B (A)　　E (D)

2. Re-store to　me　the　joy of your sal - va - tion.　Up-hold

B (A)　A (G)　　B (A)　　G#m (F#m)　　C#m (Bm)

me　with　a　will - ing　spir - it.　So　I　will　teach　trans -

A (G)　　C#m (Bm)　F#m (Em)　　G#m7 (F#m7)　F#m7 (Em7)　B (A)　D.S.

gres-sors your _ ways.　And　sin -ners will re - turn_ to_　you.___　Cre -

E (D)　　B (A)　　A (G)　　B (A)　E (D)

3. You are pleased　with sin - cer - i - ty　of　heart,　not with

B (A)　　A (G)　　B (A)　G#m (F#m)　C#m (Bm) A (G)

sac -ri -fic - es　or with hol -o - causts.　My sac -ri - fice　is a bro -ken

C#m(Bm)　　F#m (Em)　　G#m7(F#m7)　F#m7 (Em7)　B (A)　D.S.

spir - it,　for　you will not re - fuse a hum - ble　heart.___　Cre -

406 The Dwelling of God Is Among You Today

Revelation 21 adapted by
Don Austin

Music by
Don Austin

Father, Make Us One

407

John 17:21
Psalm 133:1,3

Words and Music by
Rick Ridings

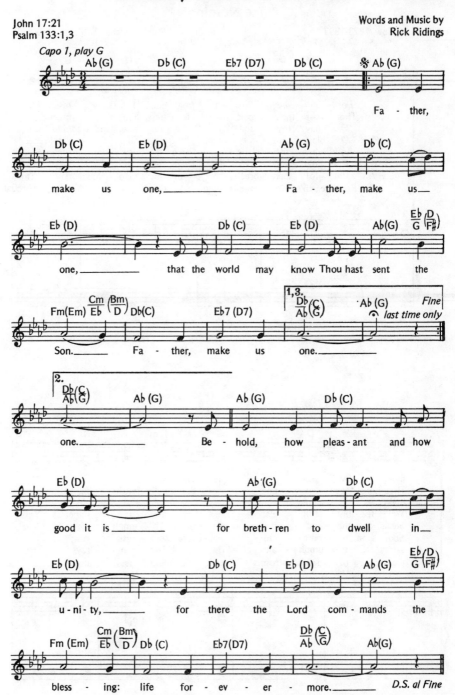

408 For All the Saints

'Sine Nomine'

William W. How, 1823-1897

Ralph Vaughan Williams, 1872-1958

1. For all the saints who from their la - bors rest, Who
2. Thou wast their rock, their for - tress, and their might;
3. O may thy sol - diers, faith - ful, true, and bold,
4. O blest com - mu - nion, fel - low - ship di - vine!
5. And when the strife is fierce, the war - fare long,
6. The gold - en eve - ning bright - ens in the west;
7. But lo! there breaks a yet more glo - rious day; The
8. From earth's wide bounds, from o - cean's far - thest coast, Through

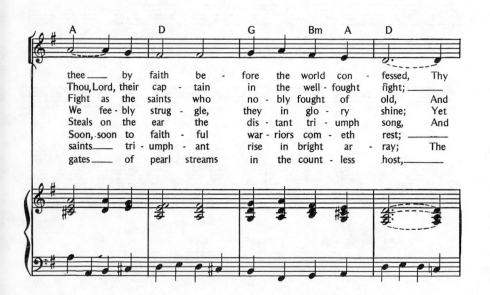

thee by faith be - fore the world con - fessed, Thy
Thou, Lord, their cap - tain in the well - fought fight;
Fight as the saints who no - bly fought of old, And
We fee - bly strug - gle, they in glo - ry shine; Yet
Steals on the ear the dis - tant tri - umph song, And
Soon, soon to faith - ful war - riors com - eth rest;
saints tri - umph - ant rise in bright ar - ray; The
gates of pearl streams in the count - less host,

409 Go Forth in Great Confidence

Words and Music by
Stacy Whitfield

VERSES

1. Sol - diers pre - par - ing for war, a-
2. Who is the cap-tain of your ar - my?
3. Robed in the strength of your God and
4. God a - lone is your Rock, a
5. Know, too, the love of your breth-ren,

noint - ed with pow-er by your King, Now gird up the
Let Him ride out a - head of you, Pre - par - ing the
clothed in the ar - mor He pro-vides, Is there one to
For - tress for you in time of need, And He is the
let it en - cour - age you, For though you go

loins of your minds that you may be ful - ly pre-pared.
path you are to take, then rid - ing a - long - side of you.
o - ver-come you? No, you shall not be dis-turbed at all. } Go
source of your strength; with - out Him you could not suc-ceed.
forth from their midst, still you re - main one with them.

REFRAIN

forth now in great con-fi-dence for you shall not be put down!

not be put down, for your God goes forth with you. You shall not, shall not be put down!

410 Great Is Thy Faithfulness

'Faithfulness'

Thomas O. Chisholm   William M. Runyan

VERSES

1. Great is Thy faith - ful-ness, O God my Fa - ther, There is no
2. Sum - mer and win - ter, and spring-time and har - vest, Sun, moon and
3. Par - don for sin and a peace that en - dur - eth, Thy own dear

411 He's Able

Words and Music by
Paul E. Paino

He's a-ble, He's a-ble, I know He is a-ble, I

know my Lord is a-ble to car-ry me through._ He's _ He _

heals the bro-ken heart-ed, and He sets the cap-tives free. He

helps the lame to walk a-gain, and He makes the blind to see. He's

412 His Name Is Wonderful

by Audrey Mieir

His Name Is Won-der-ful, ___ His Name Is Won-der ful, His Name Is

413 How Great Thou Art

by Stuart K. Hine

VERSES
Capo 1, Play A

1. O Lord my God! When I in awe-some won-der Con-sid-er all the *worlds Thy hands have made, ___ I see the stars, I hear the *roll-ing thun-der, Thy pow'r through-out the u-ni-verse dis-played,___
2. When through the woods and for-est glades I wan-der And hear the birds sing sweet-ly in the trees; ___ When I look down from loft-y moun-tain gran-deur And hear the brook and feel the gen-tle breeze;___
3. And when I think that God, His Son not spar-ing, Sent Him to die I scarce can take it in; ___ That on the cross, my bur-den glad-ly bear-ing, He bled and died to take a-way my sin; ___
4. When Christ shall come with shout of ac-cla-ma-tion And take me home, what joy shall fill my heart! ___ Then I shall bow in hum-ble ad-o-ra-tion And there pro-claim, my God, how great Thou art! ___

REFRAIN

Then sings my soul, my Sav-ior God to Thee; How great Thou art,___ how great Thou art! ___ Then sings my soul, my Sav-ior God to Thee; How great Thou art, ___ how great Thou art!

*Composer's original words were "works" and "mighty."

414 Let the Righteous Be Glad

Psalm 68 adapted by
Mark B. Foster

Music by
Mark B. Foster

Capo 3, Play Bm

1. Let God a-rise, let his en-e-mies be scat-tered; let those who hate him flee be-fore him! As smoke is driv-en, so drive them a-way; As wax melts be-fore the fire.

REFRAIN

Let the right-eous be glad, ex-ult-ing be-fore God ju-bi-lant with joy! Sing to God, sing prais-es to his name, lift up a song to him who rides up-on the clouds. clouds. Let the clouds. Lift up a song to him who rides up-on the clouds.

VERSES

2. O God when you went forth be-fore your peo-ple, when you marched through the wil-der-ness, the earth quaked, the heav-ens poured down rain at the pres-ence of the God of Is-ra-el. Let the

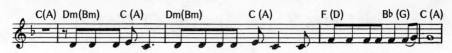

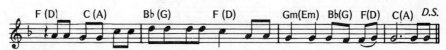

3. With might-y char-iots, thou-sands up-on thou-sands, the Lord came to the ho-ly place.

You as-cend-ed lead-ing cap-tives in your train, And re - ceiv - ing gifts a- mong men. Let the

4. Sum-mon your might, O God, show forth your strength, you who have con-quered for us.

Our God is a God of sal-va-tion; to him be-longs es - cape from death. Let the

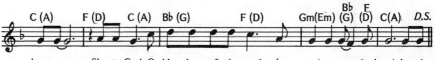

5. He sends forth his voice, his might-y voice, he who rides in the an - cient

heav-ens. Sing to God, O king-doms of the earth; sing prais-es to the Lord. Let the

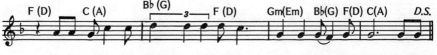

6. Awe-some is the Lord in his sanc-tu - a-ry, whose maj-es-ty is o - ver Is - ra-el.

He gives pow-er and strength to his peo-ple; bless-ed be our God! Let the

415 Lift Up Your Heads, O Gates

Psalm 24 adapted by
Martha Ilgenfritz

Music by
Martha Ilgenfritz

REFRAIN

up, lift up your heads, O— gates, And be

lift - ed up, O an - cient doors, _____ Lift

up, lift up your heads, O— gates, That the

King of Glo - ry may _ come in. _____ 1. The in. _____ Lift

VERSES

(1.) earth is the Lord's and the ful - ness there - of, The

world and those who dwell there - in, _____ For

he has found - ed it up - on the ___ seas And es -

416   The Lord Is My Shepherd

Psalm 23

Music by
Donald E. Fishel

The Lord is my shep-herd;___ there is

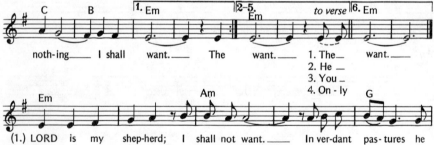

noth-ing___ I shall want.___ The want.___ 1. The___ want.

2-5.

6.

1. The___
2. He —
3. You —
4. On - ly

(1.) LORD is my shep-herd; I shall not want.___ In ver-dant pas-tures he

gives me re - pose;_____ Be-side___ rest - ful wa-ters he

leads me; he re - fresh es, re - fresh-es my soul. _____ The

(2.) guides me in right paths for his name's sake. E-ven though I walk in the

dark _____ val - ley _____ I fear no e - vil; for you are at my

side With your rod and your staff that give me cour-age. _____ The

(3.) spread the ta - ble be - fore me _____ in the sight, _____ the

sight of my foes; _____ You a - noint my head _____ with

oil; my _____ cup, _____ my cup o - ver - flows. _____ The

(4.) good-ness and kind - ness fol-low me _____ all the days, all the

days of my life; _____ And I shall dwell in the house of the

LORD _____ for _____ years, _____ for years _____ to come. _____ The

417 The Lord Reigns

Psalm 97 adapted by
Ted Kennedy III

Music by
Ted Kennedy III

REFRAIN

The Lord reigns, _____ the Lord reigns, _____
The Lord reigns, _____ the

_____ the Lord _____ reigns on earth. The
Lord reigns, _____ the Lord reigns on earth.

2-6. ... to verse 7.(after verse 5) ... D.S. al Coda
earth. _____ earth. _____ The

{ 1.
  2. His
  3. The
  4.
  5. The }

2-6. ... to verse 7. (after verse 5) ... D.S. al Coda
earth. _____ earth. _____ The

{ 1.
  2. His
  3. The
  4.
  5. The }

VERSES

1. Clouds and thick dark-ness sur-round Him; He reigns up-on His throne.

Fire goes be-fore Him and burns up His foes 'round a - bout! _____ The

(2.) light-nings light-en the world; the earth sees and trem-bles! _____

418 Mighty Is Our God

Words and Music by
Steve Alaniz

O For a Thousand Tongues to Sing 419

'Azmon'

Charles Wesley, 1707-1778

Carl G. Glaser, 1784-1829
Arr. Lowell Mason, 1792-1872

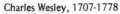

1. O for a thou - sand tongues to sing My
2. My gra - cious Mas - ter and my God, As -
3. Je - sus! the name that charms our fears, That
4. He breaks the power of can - celed sin, He
5. He speaks, and listen - ing to his voice, New
6. Hear him, ye deaf; his praise, ye dumb, Your

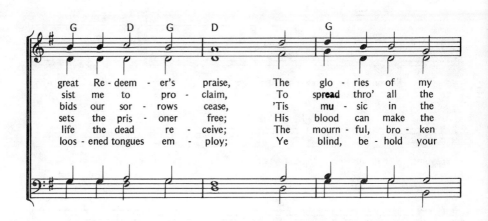

great Re - deem - er's praise, The glo - ries of my
sist me to pro - claim, To spread thro' all the
bids our sor - rows cease, 'Tis mu - sic in the
sets the pris - oner free; His blood can make the
life the dead re - ceive; The mourn - ful, bro - ken
loos - ened tongues em - ploy; Ye blind, be - hold your

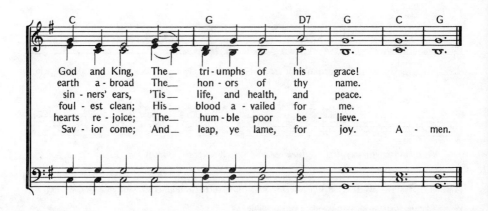

God and King, The__ tri - umphs of his grace!
earth a - broad The__ hon - ors of thy name.
sin - ners' ears, 'Tis__ life, and health, and peace.
foul - est clean, His__ blood a - vailed for me.
hearts re - joice; The__ hum - ble poor be - lieve.
Sav - ior come; And__ leap, ye lame, for joy. A - men.

420 O, Let the Redeemed

Words from Psalm 107
Adapted by Gerald Custer

Music by
Gerald Custer

Words adapted from the Revised Standard Version Bible.

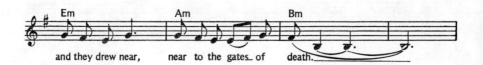

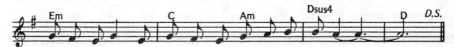

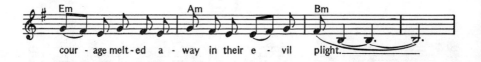

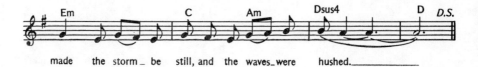

421 Praise the Lord, O My Soul

Psalm 146

Music by
Donald E. Fishel

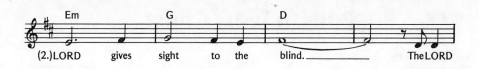

(2.) LORD gives sight to the blind._____ The LORD

rais - es up___ those that were bowed down;___ the

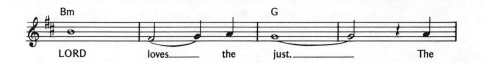

LORD loves___ the just._____ The

LORD pro - tects___ stran - gers._____ *D.S.*

(3.) fa - ther - less___ and the wid - ow he sus - tains,_____ but the

way of the wick - ed he thwarts._____ The

LORD shall reign___ for - ev - er;_____ your God, O

Zi - on, through all gen - er - a - tions. Al - le - lu - ia. *D.S.*

422 Put On Jesus Christ

Adapted from Romans 13:11-14 by
George Misulia

Music by
George Misulia

REFRAIN

Put on Je-sus Christ;— we were dark-ness, now we are light,— live in day-light,— not in the night. Put on Je-sus Christ.— Je-sus Christ.— Je-sus Christ.—

VERSES

1. You know the time has come;— we must rise up now.— Our sal-va-tion is near-er than— when we first be-lieved.—

2. Night is al-most o-ver,— day-light is at hand;— leave be-hind all the things— we did in the shad-ow of the night.—

3. Put on Je-sus Christ;— in him we have vic-to-ry,— for he shat-tered the pow'r of the night, and he's ris-en in glo-ri-ous maj-es-ty.—

Rise Up, O Men of God

423

'Festal Song'

William Pierson Merrill

William H. Walter

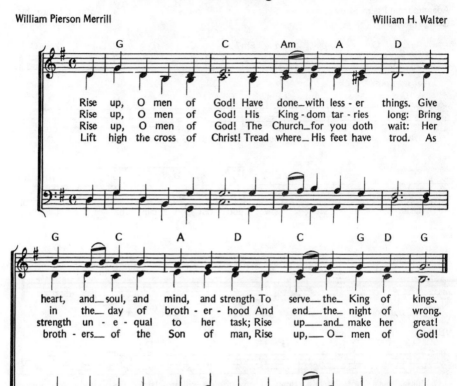

1. Rise up, O men of God! Have done with less-er things. Give heart, and soul, and mind, and strength To serve the King of kings.
2. Rise up, O men of God! His King-dom tar-ries long: Bring in the day of broth-er-hood And end the night of wrong.
3. Rise up, O men of God! The Church for you doth wait: Her strength un-e-qual to her task; Rise up and make her great!
4. Lift high the cross of Christ! Tread where His feet have trod. As broth-ers of the Son of man, Rise up, O men of God!

424 Taste and See

Adapted from Psalm 34 by
George Misulia

Words and Music by
George Misulia

REFRAIN

Taste and see how good our God can be,_____ O___ taste and see how good our God can be. 1. I will 2. Come_ 3. The_ 4. O___

good our God can be. Oh__ good our God can be._____

VERSES

(1.) bless the Lord at all times; my mouth will pro-claim His_ praise, my soul makes its boast in the Lord, our God. Let the hum-ble hear and be glad. D.S.

(2.) glo-ri-fy the Lord with_ me, to-geth-er let us praise his_ name. Look to him and grow bright in his ra-di-ant light and your face will nev-er be a-shamed. D.S.

(3.) eyes of the Lord are on the just, and his ear toward all their_ cries. The

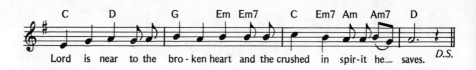

Lord is near to the bro-ken heart and the crushed in spir-it he— saves. *D.S.*

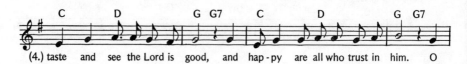

(4.) taste and see the Lord is good, and hap-py are all who trust in him. O

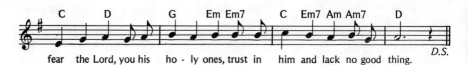

fear the Lord, you his ho-ly ones, trust in him and lack no good thing. *D.S.*

425

Thou Dost Keep Him
in Perfect Peace

Isaiah 26:3,4 adapted by
Gerald Custer

Music by
Gerald Custer

Copo 3, play D

Thy Loving Kindness 426

Psalm 63:3-4

Words and Music by
Hugh Mitchell

Thy lov-ing kind - ness____ is bet-ter than life.
hands up____ in__ Thy name.

Thy lov-ing kind - ness____ is bet-ter than life.
I lift my hands up____ in__ Thy name. } My lips shall

praise Thee,____ thus will I bless Thee:____ I 'will lift up my

hands in Thy name. 1. I lift my 2. name.____

427 We Are Men of Jesus Christ

Words and Music by
James Berlucchi

This song is meant to be sung in two parts by men only. On the rare occasion that it is sung in a mixed group, women may sing the descant on the refrain and join in on the third verse.

2. We strug-gle not a-gainst mere flesh and blood,— but strive with dark do-min-ions a-

bove. Our wea-pons mold-ed not by hu-man hands— but by the

pow'r of Christ Je-sus, we stand hold-ing the sword of the Spir-it in hand.

He is the Word of God._____ *D.S.*

3. To Christ our King we of-fer all our lives,— a fra-grant of-fring and sac-ri-

fice. To live is Christ, to die is gain for us.— Tri-um-phant

prais-es to God we sing. Re-joice in vic-t'ry with Christ, the King.

He is the Word of God._____ *D.S. al Coda*

Come and take your stand.____ Come and take your stand.____

Come and take your stand.____ Come and take your stand.____

____ Serve the Word of God._____

____ Serve the Word of God._____

428

You Are Holy

Words adapted from Rev. 4:8,11
by Donald E. Fishel

Music by
Donald E. Fishel

CUMULATIVE INDEX

The songs numbered 1 through 79 are in *Songs of Praise, Vol. 1;* numbers 201 through 241 are in *Songs of Praise, Vol. 2;* numbers 301 through 339 are in *Songs of Praise Vol. 3;* numbers 401 through 428 are in *Songs of Praise Vol. 4.*